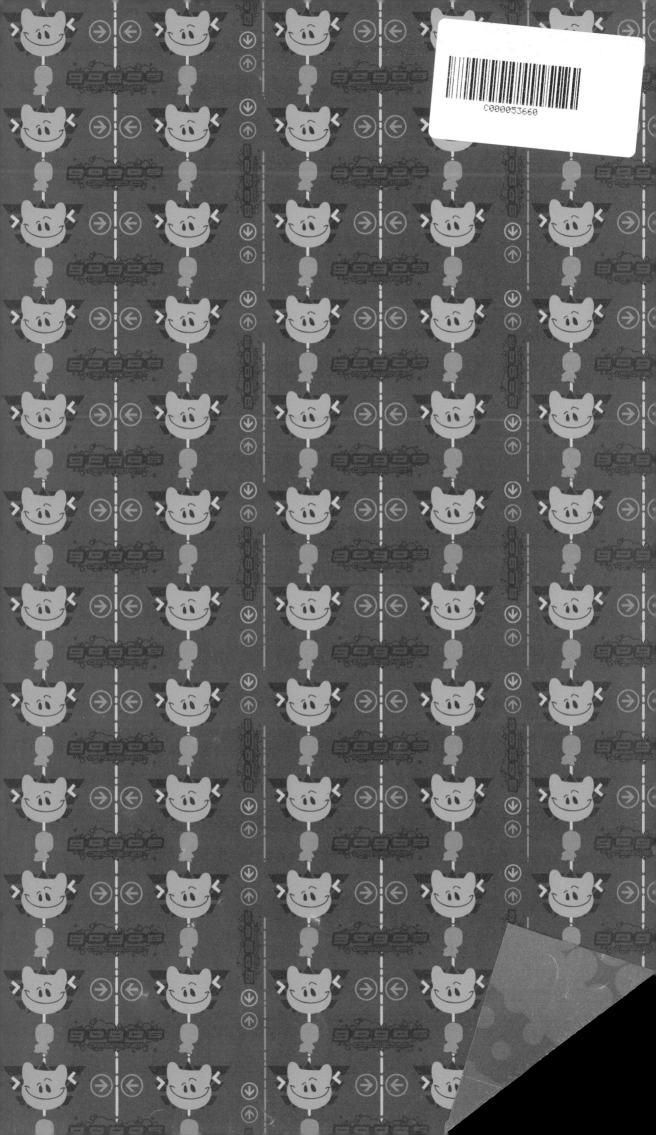

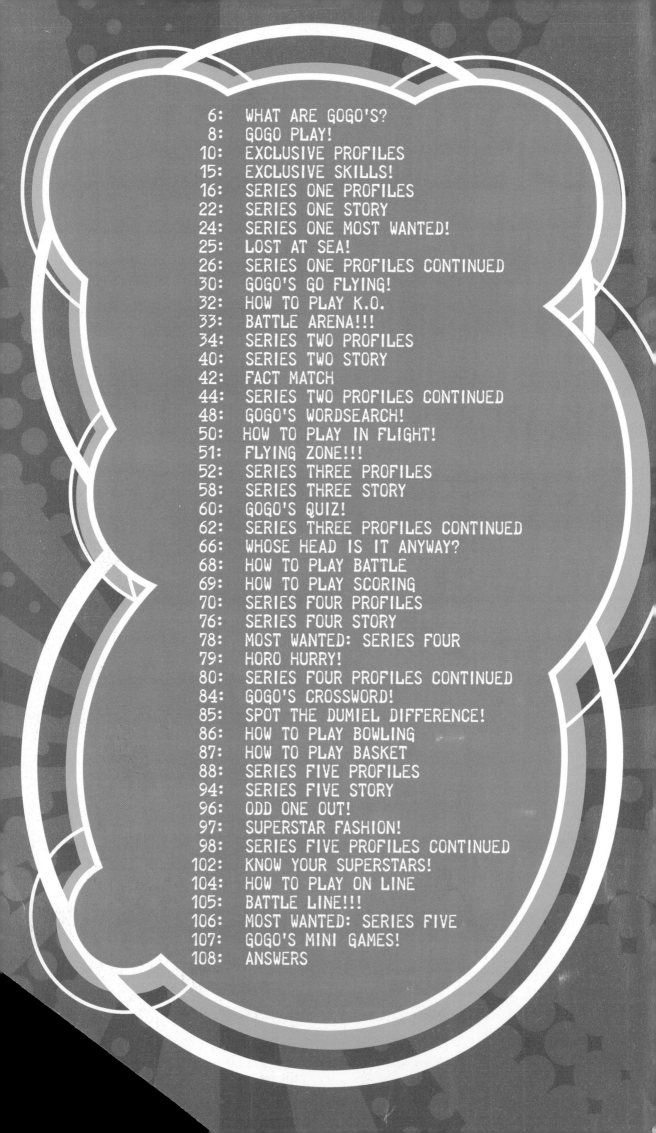

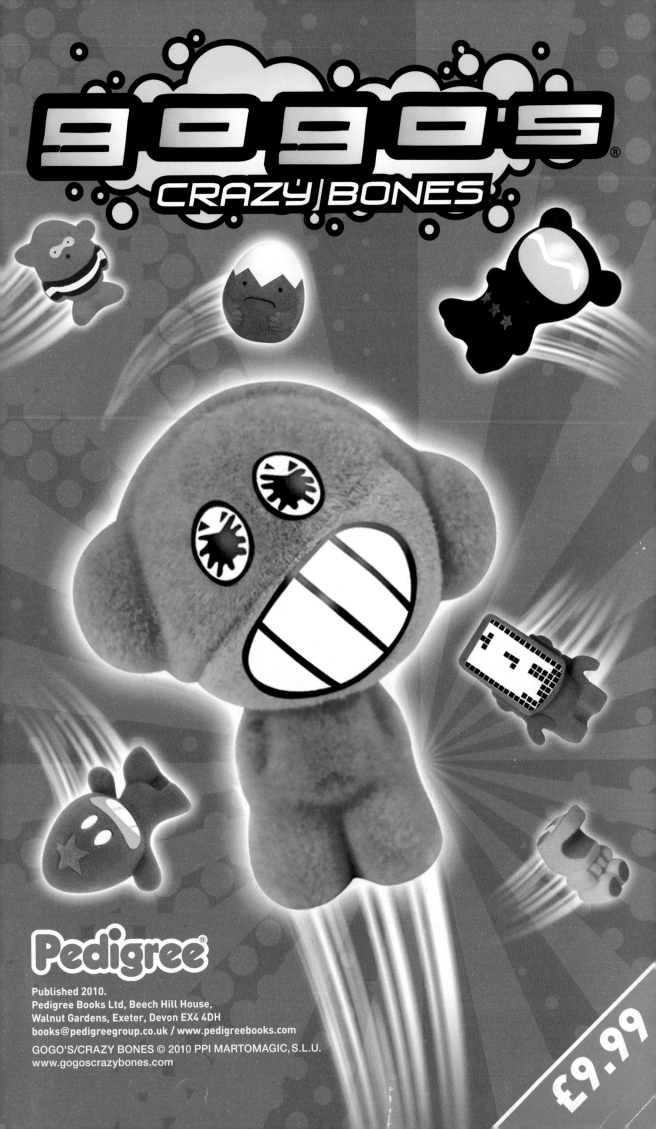

gogo's
CRAZY BONES

Pedigree

Published 2010.
Pedigree Books Ltd, Beech Hill House,
Walnut Gardens, Exeter, Devon EX4 4DH
books@pedigreegroup.co.uk / www.pedigreebooks.com

£9.99

GOGO'S CRAZY BONES ARE SMALL BEINGS THAT HAVE SPREAD ACROSS THE GLOBE. NOBODY KNOWS WHERE THEY CAME FROM AND NOBODY KNOWS THEIR PURPOSE OF BEING HERE.

THEY ARE MISCHEVIOUS LITTLE CREATURES WHO LIKE TO EXPLORE AND LOVE TO PLAY. THEIR ANTICS ARE CHEEKY AND AMUSING AND EACH INDIVIDUAL GOGO HAS A CHARACTER OF ITS OWN.

JUST TO MAKE THEM ESPECIALLY UNIQUE, EACH GOGO IS AVAILABLE IN DIFFERENT COLOURS — SO YOU COULD COLLECT A GANG OF GOGO'S IN YOUR FAVOURITE COLOUR!

EACH GOGO HAS A SPECIAL ABILITY, WHICH SEPARATES IT FROM THE REST — LOOK FOR THESE IN THE PROFILE PAGES LATER IN THIS BOOK.

IN THOSE PAGES YOU WILL ALSO FIND INFORMATION ABOUT THEIR SKILLS, EXPERTISE AND FEARS.

GOGO'S?

THERE ARE THOSE WHO DREAM OF SPACE,
OTHERS WHO LOVE TO RUN LIKE THE WIND,

WHILE SOME SIMPLY LIKE TO EAT SWEETS!
IN THAT SENSE, THEY'RE A LOT LIKE YOU AND I!

THEY ARE DESIGNED SO YOU CAN HOLD
AND THROW THEM WITH ONE FINGER AT
THE BACK OF THE GOGO — IF YOU LOOK
CLOSELY YOU CAN SEE EACH GOGO'S
UNIQUE NUMBER ON THE BACK, TOO.

YOU WILL ALSO
FIND THE OFFICIAL MAGIC BOX
INT STAMP ON THE BACK, WHICH
CONFIRMS THAT YOUR GOGO'S ARE
ORIGINAL AND OF THE HIGHEST QUALITY!

MAGIC BOX INT.

GOGO

THE MOST IMPORTANT THINGS TO GOGO'S, MORE THAN FOOD AND SLEEP, IS PLAYING.

EACH HAS THEIR OWN FAVOURITE GAME, WHICH THEY PERFORM BEST IN — THIS GIVES YOU GUIDANCE AS TO WHICH GOGO'S TO CHOOSE WHEN PLAYING WITH YOUR FRIENDS.

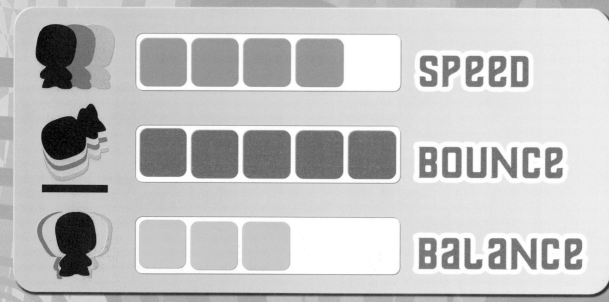

SPEED

BOUNCE

BALANCE

SERIES ONE GOGO'S HAVE SPECIFIC SKILL POINTS FOR EACH OF THE THREE KEY AREAS FOR PLAYING — SPEED, BOUNCE AND BALANCE.

SPEED, OBVIOUSLY, REFLECTS THE PACE AT WHICH THEY FLY; BOUNCE TELLS YOU IF IT'S EASY TO PREDICT WHERE THE GOGO WILL LAND; AND BALANCE REVEALS THE CHANCES OF IT LANDING ON ITS FEET AFTER BEING THROWN.

PLAY! ★★

IN SERIES TWO, THE GOGO'S HAVE EVOLVED — USE THE EVOLUTION BAR TO SEE JUST HOW MUCH THEY HAVE EVOLVED AND IMPROVED!

EVOLUTION

SERIES THREE GOGO'S ARE 'EXPLORERS'. THEIR CURIOSITY AND LOVE OF ADVENTURE TAKES THEM ON MANY EXCITING MISSIONS!

SERIES FOUR INTRODUCES 'POWER' GOGO'S. THESE GUYS ARE THE CRAZIEST GOGO'S EVER!

SERIES FIVE IS LIKE A GOGO HALL OF FAME — BRINGING TOGETHER THE 'SUPERSTARS' FROM THE PREVIOUS FOUR SERIES!

You can find more details on all of the Gogo's from each series, plus the exclusive Gogo's attached to the side of your annual, in the profile pages.

☆ EXCLUSIVE

ANUIK

DOESN'T HAVE A NEGATIVE ANSWER FOR ANYBODY, HIS BIG HEART MAKES HIM VERY FRIENDLY.

FAVOURITE GAME:

ABILITY

SUPER EAR

SPEED

BALANCE

BOUNCE

10

GOGO'S! ⭐⭐⭐

BLEM

ALTHOUGH HE HAS A DEVIL FACE, HE'S VERY KIND WITH HIS FRIENDS.

FAVOURITE GAME:
online

ABILITY
CHARGE

SPEED

BALANCE

BOUNCE

☆ EXCLUSIVE

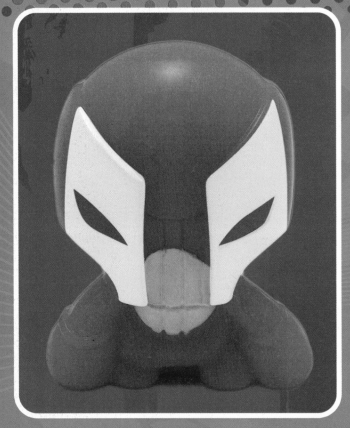

PLANK

THANKS TO HIS NIGHT VISION, PLANK WILL ALWAYS FIND YOU. YOU CAN'T ESCAPE!

FAVOURITE GAME:

ABILITY

NIGHT VISION

SPEED

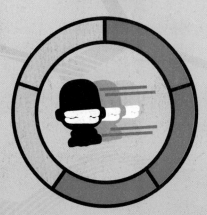

BALANCE

BOUNCE

GOGO'S! ⭐⭐⭐

K-CUL

DOESN'T SEE THINGS VERY CLEARLY. ALTHOUGH HE IS NOT VERY GOOD LOOKING, HE IS VERY FRIENDLY.

FAVOURITE GAME:

ABILITY

POWERFUL EYEBROW

SPEED	BALANCE	BOUNCE

☆ exclusive

KaRIN

THE GURU GOGO COMES FROM THE MOUNTAINS. WITH HIS SECRET POTIONS HE CAN TRANSFORM YOU INTO A GOGO!

FAVOURITE GAME:

ABILITY

GOGO POTION

SPEED

BALANCE

BOUNCE

GOGO'S! ★★★

EXCLUSIVE SKILLS!

USING THE SKILL POINTS SPECIFIED IN THE PROFILES OVER THE PAST FIVE PAGES, ANSWER THE GOGO 'BATTLE' QUESTIONS BELOW!

1. WHICH EXCLUSIVE GOGO HAS THE BEST BALANCE?

2. OF THE EXCLUSIVE GOGO'S YOU'VE RECEIVED WITH THIS ANNUAL, WHICH HAS THE BEST BOUNCE?

3. IF YOU WERE TO SEE WHICH OF THESE EXCLUSIVES WERE QUICKEST, WHICH TWO WOULD WIN THAT RACE?

4. WHO IS MORE RELIABLE TO BOUNCE, PLANK OR K-CUL?

5. AND WHICH OF THOSE IS FASTER?

Profiles

1 MOSH

SUPER KIND. ALL THE GOGO'S WANT TO BE FRIENDS WITH MOSH.

SPEED

BOUNCE

BALANCE

SPECIAL ABILITY: MAGIC SMILE

FAVOURITE GAME: K.O.

2 NASAKO

ALWAYS COOL BECAUSE HE HAS A SPECIAL SCORING TECHNIQUE.

SPEED

BOUNCE

BALANCE

SPECIAL ABILITY: DOUBLE FAST HOOK

FAVOURITE GAME: BATTLE

3 SATO

READY FOR THE FIGHT. WHERE IS THE RING?

SPEED

BOUNCE

BALANCE

SPECIAL ABILITY: K.O. PUNCH

FAVOURITE GAME: BATTLE

4 OKORI

NOBODY KNOWS WHAT HE EATS, BUT WHATEVER IT IS, IT ISN'T DOING HIM ANY GOOD.

SPEED

BOUNCE

BALANCE

SPECIAL ABILITY: EATING

FAVOURITE GAME: SCORING

5 TORI

CLEVER AND FUN. LIKES TO BE THE BOSS.

SPEED

BOUNCE

BALANCE

SPECIAL ABILITY: JUMPS WALLS

FAVOURITE GAME: SCORING

6 HELLY

THE FASTEST GOGO. HIS HELMET HELPS HIM TO GO BREATHTAKINGLY FAST.

SPEED

BOUNCE

BALANCE

SPECIAL ABILITY: CONTINUOUS SPRINT

FAVOURITE GAME: ON LINE

7 SKULL

HE LOOKS MYSTERIOUS AND WHEN YOU LEAST EXPECT IT, HE'LL DO SOMETHING FUNNY TO MAKE YOU JUMP.

SPEED

BOUNCE

BALANCE

SPECIAL ABILITY: SPOOKY SKILLS

FAVOURITE GAME: BASKET

8 ANGIRU

TELL ANGIRU YOUR SECRETS AND THEY WILL BE SAFE FOREVER.

SPEED

BOUNCE

BALANCE

SPECIAL ABILITY: KEEPS SECRETS

FAVOURITE GAME: BASKET

gogo's CRAZY BONES

9 UMU

LIKES TO VISIT THE SWIMMING POOL EVERYDAY TO THINK UP NEW IDEAS.

SPEED
BOUNCE
BALANCE

SPECIAL ABILITY:
INTELLIGENT SWIMMING

FAVOURITE GAME:
IN FLIGHT

10 AIKO

THE GOGO WITH THE BEST SENSE OF SMELL. CAN DETECT A SMELL FROM A MILE AWAY.

SPEED
BOUNCE
BALANCE

SPECIAL ABILITY:
WONDER NOSE

FAVOURITE GAME:
IN FLIGHT

11 ICHIRO

DON'T STARE INTO HIS EYES. YOU'LL BE OVERCOME BY HIS GREAT MENTAL POWER.

SPEED
BOUNCE
BALANCE

SPECIAL ABILITY:
DAGGER EYES

FAVOURITE GAME:
BOWLING

12 NUCLOS

ABSORBS POLLUTION AND LEAVES THE AIR REALLY CLEAN.

SPEED
BOUNCE
BALANCE

SPECIAL ABILITY:
POLLUTION REDUCTION

FAVOURITE GAME:
K.O.

13 BOY

SPEED
BOUNCE
BALANCE

SPECIAL ABILITY:
SENSORY SPACE RADAR

FAVOURITE GAME:
BASKET

THE BEST BLINDFOLDED RUNNER. HE NEVER FALLS OVER.

14 NEKO

SPEED
BOUNCE
BALANCE

SPECIAL ABILITY:
FLAME CATCHER

FAVOURITE GAME:
ON LINE

USES ITS BODY TO PROTECT OTHER GOGO'S FROM FIRE.

15 HAZARD

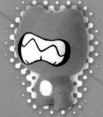

SPEED
BOUNCE
BALANCE

SPECIAL ABILITY:
COURAGE

FAVOURITE GAME:
K.O.

WHEN FACED WITH DANGER, IT JUST GRITS ITS TEETH AND CARRIES ON.

16 SUN

FIRES A RAY OF OPTIMISM AT EVERY GOGO IN HIS PATH.

SPEED
BOUNCE
BALANCE

SPECIAL ABILITY:
HAPPY RAY

FAVOURITE GAME:
K.O.

Profiles

HIRO

SOLVES PROBLEMS WITH ELECTRIFYING 500W IDEAS.

SPEED

BOUNCE

BALANCE

SPECIAL ABILITY: ELECTRIC IDEAS

FAVOURITE GAME: IN FLIGHT

AKA

CAN COLLIDE WITH 100 GOGO'S WITHOUT GETTING ANY BUMPS OR BRUISES.

SPEED

BOUNCE

BALANCE

SPECIAL ABILITY: HAMMER HEAD

FAVOURITE GAME: BOWLING

MOLLY

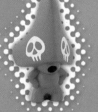

GETTING ANGRY IS NO PROBLEM BECAUSE IT LASTS FOR LESS THAN ONE SECOND!

SPEED

BOUNCE

BALANCE

SPECIAL ABILITY: MICRO-ANGER

FAVOURITE GAME: K.O.

NARI

DON'T TRY AND STARE OUT NARI — YOU WILL LOSE.

SPEED

BOUNCE

BALANCE

SPECIAL ABILITY: CONCENTRATION

FAVOURITE GAME: IN FLIGHT

SIMI

SMILING CHARGES UP HIS POWERS. HE SMILES AND THEN SHOOTS AWAY.

SPEED

BOUNCE

BALANCE

SPECIAL ABILITY: POWER SMILES

FAVOURITE GAME: BATTLE

CODI

ALWAYS CONNECTED. ASK IT ANYTHING AND THE DATA WILL BE DOWNLOADED.

SPEED

BOUNCE

BALANCE

SPECIAL ABILITY: QUICK CONNECTION

FAVOURITE GAME: IN FLIGHT

HIRAKU

THE MOST DARING PIRATE — ENDLESS ADVENTURES.

SPEED

BOUNCE

BALANCE

SPECIAL ABILITY: BOARDING

FAVOURITE GAME: BOWLING

RUFUS

SEES THINGS OTHERS CAN'T USING THE POWER OF PLANET X.

SPEED

BOUNCE

BALANCE

SPECIAL ABILITY: X-VISION

FAVOURITE GAME: IN FLIGHT

 25 TEMP

IS THE WATER REALLY COLD? WHAT TIME IS IT GOING TO RAIN? JUST ASK TEMP.

SPEED

BOUNCE

BALANCE

SPECIAL ABILITY: WATER FORECASTING

FAVOURITE GAME: ON LINE

 26 PIBI

ORGANISES IDEAS IN BOTH SIDES OF ITS HEAD. NEED IDEAS? SPEAK TO PIBI.

SPEED

BOUNCE

BALANCE

SPECIAL ABILITY: DOUBLE BRAIN

FAVOURITE GAME: BASKET

 27 DARE

THE BEST LOOKING GOGO. HE ALWAYS LOOKS HIS BEST.

SPEED

BOUNCE

BALANCE

SPECIAL ABILITY: PHOTOGENIC

FAVOURITE GAME: BATTLE

 28 DANKO

FELINE FAST, AGILE AND WELL BEHAVED.

SPEED

BOUNCE

BALANCE

SPECIAL ABILITY: CUTE AND CUDDLY

FAVOURITE GAME: BOWLING

 29 MC TOY

ALWAYS CAREFUL AND QUESTIONING. NEVER MAKES A WRONG MOVE.

SPEED

BOUNCE

BALANCE

SPECIAL ABILITY: NO MISTAKES

FAVOURITE GAME: IN FLIGHT

 30 GAIJI

TAKES CONTROL OF THE SITUATION. AN EXPERT IN CROWD CONTROL.

SPEED

BOUNCE

BALANCE

SPECIAL ABILITY: BATTLE HELMET

FAVOURITE GAME: BATTLE

31 LESSI

SOMETIMES FEELS A LITTLE LOW. YOU MIGHT NEED TO PERK HIM UP.

SPEED

BOUNCE

BALANCE

SPECIAL ABILITY: SHOCK ABSORBER

FAVOURITE GAME: K.O.

 32 POP

LOVES MUSIC AND DANCES NON-STOP.

SPEED

BOUNCE

BALANCE

SPECIAL ABILITY: TOP RHYTHM

FAVOURITE GAME: ON LINE

33 IMON

SPEED
BOUNCE
BALANCE

SPECIAL ABILITY:
MENTAL STRENGTH

FAVOURITE GAME:
BATTLE

ABSORBS IDEAS
THROUGH ITS STAR.

34 JELLY

SPEED
BOUNCE
BALANCE

SPECIAL ABILITY:
SUPER WARRIOR

FAVOURITE GAME:
BATTLE

BRAVE ENOUGH FOR
ANY BATTLE.

35 SUMON

SPEED
BOUNCE
BALANCE

SPECIAL ABILITY:
MOUTH CAGE

FAVOURITE GAME:
BOWLING

TRAPS ENEMIES INSIDE HIS
HUGE POWERFUL JAWS.

36 CHO

SPEED
BOUNCE
BALANCE

SPECIAL ABILITY:
ENERGY

FAVOURITE GAME:
BATTLE

RACES AHEAD AT FULL SPEED
AND THAT'S WHY HE DOESN'T
HAVE ANY TEETH LEFT

37 RAYSUN

SPEED
BOUNCE
BALANCE

SPECIAL ABILITY:
SUN RAY

FAVOURITE GAME:
BOWLING

HAS A
GREAT TIME
BRINGING
SUNSHINE
INTO THE
GOGO'S
WORLD.

38 FIST

SPEED
BOUNCE
BALANCE

SPECIAL ABILITY:
ULTIMATE GRIP

FAVOURITE GAME:
BASKET

HOLDS A SECRET STRENGTH
INSIDE HIS FIST.

39 ZAR-ZAR

SPEED
BOUNCE
BALANCE

SPECIAL ABILITY:
CUNNING

FAVOURITE GAME:
BASKET

PRETENDS
NOT TO
UNDERSTAND
BUT KNOWS
MUCH MORE
THAN YOU
THINK.

40 HAYATO

SPEED
BOUNCE
BALANCE

SPECIAL ABILITY:
SUPER WINK

FAVOURITE GAME:
BASKET

WANTS 20
MIRRORS
NEARBY
TO KEEP
AN EYE ON
EVERYTHING.

41 BIGU

SPEED

BOUNCE

BALANCE

STANDS TALL AND UPRIGHT. GIVES FUN ORDERS TO THE TROOPS.

SPECIAL ABILITY:
FUN ORDERS

FAVOURITE GAME:
K.O.

42 OJARU

SPEED

BOUNCE

BALANCE

SPECIAL ABILITY:
FLYING EARS

FAVOURITE GAME:
IN FLIGHT

BADLY SEWN TOGETHER BUT STRONG ENOUGH TO HOLD THE SECRET OF FLIGHT.

43 SPEED

SPEED

BOUNCE

BALANCE

TURNS HIS HEAD WITH SUPERSONIC SPEED AND ALWAYS SEES THE WORLD AROUND HIM.

SPECIAL ABILITY:
PANORAMIC VIEW

FAVOURITE GAME:
ON LINE

44 TREMI

SPEED

BOUNCE

BALANCE

APPEARANCES CAN BE DECEIVING. NOT AS GRUMPY AS HE LOOKS.

SPECIAL ABILITY:
LAUGHTER MASK

FAVOURITE GAME:
BATTLE

45 B-BOY

SPEED

BOUNCE

BALANCE

SPECIAL ABILITY:
POPCORN ATTACK

FAVOURITE GAME:
BASKET

EATS A LOT OF POPCORN TO IMPROVE HIS BOUNCING POWER.

46 MOCHI

SPEED

BOUNCE

BALANCE

SPECIAL ABILITY:
LUCKY POWER

FAVOURITE GAME:
ON LINE

A LUCKY CHARM AMONGST THE GOGO'S FAMILY.

47 POPUS

SPEED

BOUNCE

BALANCE

SPECIAL ABILITY:
EARTH EATER

FAVOURITE GAME:
BOWLING

DIGS LONG TUNNELS TO MOVE AROUND WITHOUT ANYONE KNOWING HE IS THERE.

48 TUBE

SPEED

BOUNCE

BALANCE

SPECIAL ABILITY:
RECORD & PLAY

FAVOURITE GAME:
ON LINE

THANKS TO GRAMOPHONE EARS, IT HEARS EVERYTHING AND CAN PLAY IT ALL BACK.

THE END

MOST WANTED

THE GOGO'S THAT EVERYONE WANTS: A HANDFUL OF SUPER RARE AND ULTRACOOL GOGO'S FOR YOU TO COLLECT. THESE GOGO'S HAVE EXTRA SPECIAL DESIGNS, TOO.

THE MOST WANTED GOGO'S FOR SERIES ONE ARE:

ANGIRU

ICHIRU

HIRAKU

FIST

B-BOY

LOST AT SEA!

HIRAKU IS A DARING GOGO PIRATE, BUT HE AND HIS FRIENDS HAVE GOT LOST ON THEIR LATEST TREASURE HUNT! TO MAKE MATTERS WORSE, HIS MAP IS WET AND SOME OF THE INSTRUCTIONS HE HAD WRITTEN ON THE BACK HAVE DISAPPEARED!

CAN YOU DECODE HIRAKU'S NOTES AND HELP THE GANG FIND THE HIDDEN TREASURE?

1. GO L_F_ WHEN YOU SEE THE LIGHTH_US_.

2. THEN, GO STR__GHT FOR ABOUT _WO MILES.

3. YOU WILL SEE A DESERTED BEA__ ON YOUR R_GH_.

4. DOCK YOUR BOA_ HERE.

5. __G A HOLE ABOUT 50 METRES UP THE BEACH. YOU WILL FIND YOUR TREAS__E!

gogo's CRAZY BONES

Profiles

49 CUBIC

A ROBOT GOGO WHO IS AN EXPERT MECHANIC.

SPEED
BOUNCE
BALANCE

SPECIAL ABILITY:
REPAIRS EVERYTHING
FAVOURITE GAME:
KO

50 B-KING

WHEN HE SITS DOWN TO THINK HE ACTS LIKE A TRIBAL CHIEF.

SPEED
BOUNCE
BALANCE

SPECIAL ABILITY:
MAGIC HORNS
FAVOURITE GAME:
BATTLE

51 CROC

CROC IS A CHEQUERED CROCODILE. IN OTHER WORDS, A CROCODILE CHESS MASTER.

SPEED
BOUNCE
BALANCE

SPECIAL ABILITY:
CHECK MATE
FAVOURITE GAME:
SCORING

52 UFUS

WITH ITS RUBBER NINJA BODY IT CAN FLY LONG DISTANCES BETWEEN BOUNCES.

SPEED
BOUNCE
BALANCE

SPECIAL ABILITY:
FLYING BOUNCE
FAVOURITE GAME:
SCORING

53 EGBOT

SPEED
BOUNCE
BALANCE

SPECIAL ABILITY:
ELECTRIC JUMP
FAVOURITE GAME:
BASKET

COMMUNICATES THROUGH WAVES, THANKS TO ITS ELECTROMAGNETIC MOUTH.

54 H-83

SPEED
BOUNCE
BALANCE

SPECIAL ABILITY:
THROWS STARS
FAVOURITE GAME:
K.O.

A STRONG SHELL MAKES IT SUPER RESISTANT.

55 ATORI

KEEPS ALL HIS KNOWLEDGE SAFE INSIDE AND THEN CLOSES THE ZIP.

SPEED
BOUNCE
BALANCE

SPECIAL ABILITY:
GIGA MEMORY
FAVOURITE GAME:
K.O.

56 B-BALL

IF THE SPORT HAS A BALL, HE IS THE MASTER.

SPEED
BOUNCE
BALANCE

SPECIAL ABILITY:
BALL SKILLS
FAVOURITE GAME:
BASKET

Profiles

 USUZI

IF SOMETHING GOES WRONG, HE IS VERY NERVOUS UNTIL A SOLUTION IS FOUND.

SPEED

BOUNCE

BALANCE

SPECIAL ABILITY: CLAMP CLICK

FAVOURITE GAME: BATTLE

 ECO

CAN TRAVEL OVER ANY OBSTACLE OR DIFFICULT TERRAIN USING FOUR ARMS.

SPEED

BOUNCE

BALANCE

SPECIAL ABILITY: 4X4 RACE

FAVOURITE GAME: BASKET

 OH!

LOVES TO SURPRISE ALL THE OTHER GOGO'S.

SPEED

BOUNCE

BALANCE

SPECIAL ABILITY: HIDING

FAVOURITE GAME: IN FLIGHT

ALKALINE

ULTRA TURBO-CHARGED POWER. FULL BLAST ENERGY.

SPEED

BOUNCE

BALANCE

SPECIAL ABILITY: BATTERY CHARGER

FAVOURITE GAME: BATTLE

 AWA-SHIMA

ALWAYS READY FOR ACTION, BUT DON'T BOTHER HIM FOR ANYTHING ELSE.

SPEED

BOUNCE

BALANCE

SPECIAL ABILITY: GRAFFITI-FLASH

FAVOURITE GAME: K.O.

 GHOST

DARK MYSTERY, NOT EVERYONE DARES LOOK HIM IN THE FACE.

SPEED

BOUNCE

BALANCE

SPECIAL ABILITY: FRIGHTENING WHISPER

FAVOURITE GAME: BASKET

 TUT

THE CURIOUS MUMMY. CAN REMOVE A TINY BIT OF BANDAGE TO SEE WHAT'S GOING ON.

SPEED

BOUNCE

BALANCE

SPECIAL ABILITY: HEALING

FAVOURITE GAME: K.O.

 MATSUE

VERY PROUD OF HIS SUPER COOL HAIR CUT.

SPEED

BOUNCE

BALANCE

SPECIAL ABILITY: SOFT FRINGE

FAVOURITE GAME: IN FLIGHT

65 AKITA

FRIEND AND LOYAL COMPANION, YOU CAN COUNT ON AKITA.

SPEED

BOUNCE

BALANCE

SPECIAL ABILITY: ANTENNA HORN

FAVOURITE GAME: ON LINE

66 SHIZOUKA

WITH JUST ONE CRY HE CAN GET THE ATTENTION OF ALL THE GOGO'S.

SPEED

BOUNCE

BALANCE

SPECIAL ABILITY: GOGO'S ALERT

FAVOURITE GAME: K.O.

67 MYAKE

CUTS THROUGH THE WATER AT AMAZING SPEED.

SPEED

BOUNCE

BALANCE

SPECIAL ABILITY: RUDDER SHAPED CREST

FAVOURITE GAME: ON LINE

68 FUJICHIK

FLIES FAST AND HIGH, BUT LANDS SOFT AND SMOOTH.

SPEED

BOUNCE

BALANCE

SPECIAL ABILITY: INSTANT LANDING

FAVOURITE GAME: IN FLIGHT

69 TSU

JUICES, COLD DRINKS, HE ALWAYS HAS A DRINK HANDY. A THIRSTY GOGO.

SPEED

BOUNCE

BALANCE

SPECIAL ABILITY: BIG GULP

FAVOURITE GAME: BOWLING

70 KOKUBU

THE LIFE AND SOUL OF ANY PARTY. INVITED TO EVERY OCCASION.

SPEED

BOUNCE

BALANCE

SPECIAL ABILITY: FRIEND VISER

FAVOURITE GAME: BOWLING

71 IZUMI

LOVES SPEED AND NEVER GETS OFF HIS MOTORBIKE.

SPEED

BOUNCE

BALANCE

SPECIAL ABILITY: MOTORBIKE RACING

FAVOURITE GAME: ON LINE

72 AKO

THE ULTIMATE MINDER. 50 SPECIAL MOVES READY TO GO.

SPEED

BOUNCE

BALANCE

SPECIAL ABILITY: MARTIAL ARTS

FAVOURITE GAME: BATTLE

73 KAMI-KAMI

SPEED

BOUNCE

BALANCE

SPECIAL ABILITY:
SUPER BITE

FAVOURITE GAME:
SCORING

BRUSHES HIS TEETH BEFORE PLAYING ANY GAME. ALWAYS FRESH AND MINTY.

74 SAGO

SPEED

BOUNCE

BALANCE

SPECIAL ABILITY:
SELF-MOULDING

FAVOURITE GAME:
SCORING

CHANGES SHAPE TO FIT INTO ANY SPACE.

75 VAMPA

SPEED

BOUNCE

BALANCE

SPECIAL ABILITY:
LOW-LEVEL FLYING

FAVOURITE GAME:
SCORING

NOT SEEN MUCH DURING THE DAY. HE MOVES IN THE DARK.

76 MISHA

SPEED

BOUNCE

BALANCE

SPECIAL ABILITY:
MAKES YOU SLEEPY

FAVOURITE GAME:
SCORING

CUTE AND CUDDLY. THE BEST SLEEPING COMPANION AROUND.

77 YUZA

SPEED

BOUNCE

BALANCE

SPECIAL ABILITY:
WEIGHT LIFTING

FAVOURITE GAME:
K.O.

AS STRONG AS A ROCK. ARMS LIKE GRANITE.

78 TAN CHIA

SPEED

BOUNCE

BALANCE

SPECIAL ABILITY:
FREE FIGHTING

FAVOURITE GAME:
BATTLE

WANTS TO BE THE GOGO'S HERO. ALWAYS READY FOR ACTION.

79 KOLO

FUTURISTIC GOGO WHO LOVES TECHNOLOGY. FLOATS THROUGH SPACE GUIDED BY THE STARS.

SPEED

BOUNCE

BALANCE

SPECIAL ABILITY:
SPACE FLIGHT

FAVOURITE GAME:
BOWLING

80 EVI

ALTHOUGH IT TRIES TO FRIGHTEN ITS FRIENDS, IT MAKES THEM LAUGH MORE THAN ANYTHING.

SPEED

BOUNCE

BALANCE

SPECIAL ABILITY:
ATTACK OF LAUGHTER

FAVOURITE GAME:
IN FLIGHT

GOGO'S GO

OJARU, HIRO AND ALKALINE ARE HAVING A JUMPING COMPETITION, TO SEE WHO CAN GO FURTHEST.

THEY NEED YOUR HELP JUDGING THE WINNER, THOUGH, AS THEY ALL JUMPED AT THE SAME TIME!

UNTANGLE AND FOLLOW THEIR FLIGHT LINES TO SEE WHO WINS THE COMPETITION!

ALKALINE   **OJARU**   **HIRO**

FLYING!

3RD

2ND

WINNER!

31

HOW TO PLAY K.O.

A FUN GAME THAT WILL TEST YOUR ACCURACY, WHEREVER YOU PLAY IT, K.O. IS AS MUCH ABOUT YOUR AIM AS IT IS ABOUT YOUR GOGO'S FLIGHT.

BEFORE YOU USE THE 'KNOCKOUT ARENA' OPPOSITE TO PLAY THE GAME, FAMILIARISE YOURSELF WITH HOW TO PLAY K.O., BELOW:

1

Each player must place the same number of Gogo's inside the battle circle.

2

The players take it in turns to throw their Gogo's at the circle to try and knock their opponent's Gogo's out of the circle.

3

Decide who goes first by each throwing a Gogo in the air; the first person to have their Gogo land standing up will go first.

4

When it's your turn, make sure you stand at least two big steps away from the circle so it's not too easy!

5

Agree how many goes you will each have before you start.

6

The player that manages to keep the most Gogo's inside the battle arena at the end of the agreed number of throws, wins the game.

BATTLE ARENA!!!

1. MOSHI

AVOIDS CONFRONTATION. ALWAYS BRINGS THE GOODNESS AND PEACE.

SPECIAL ABILITY: PEACEMAKER
FAVOURITE GAME: K.O.

GOGO'S EVOLUTION BAR: 15

2. NASOKI

TRIES TO MAKE EVERYONE LAUGH. SOMETIMES HIS LOOKS SCARE THE OTHERS A LITTLE BIT.

SPECIAL ABILITY: JOKER
FAVOURITE GAME: BOWLING

GOGO'S EVOLUTION BAR: 11

3. SATORI

ALWAYS WATCHFUL IN CASE ACTION IS NEEDED.

SPECIAL ABILITY: WATCHFUL EYE
FAVOURITE GAME: BASKET

GOGO'S EVOLUTION BAR: 12

4. OKY

MAYBE SOME INDIGESTION GAVE HIM A MUSHROOM FACE.

SPECIAL ABILITY: FUNGUS FURY
FAVOURITE GAME: BOWLING

GOGO'S EVOLUTION BAR: 13

5. RACETOR

HE LOVES SPORTS AND CAN CALCULATE HOW TO WIN ANY RACE.

SPECIAL ABILITY: NUMERIC MEMORY
FAVOURITE GAME: SCORING

GOGO'S EVOLUTION BAR: 9

6. HELED

HE ROBOTIZED HIS BRAIN TO THINK SUPER FAST.

SPECIAL ABILITY: MENTAL DEXTERITY
FAVOURITE GAME: K.O.

GOGO'S EVOLUTION BAR: 8

7. SKER

HE'S NAÏVE AND EVERYTHING SEEMS WEIRD TO HIM.

SPECIAL ABILITY: CURIOSITY
FAVOURITE GAME: IN FLIGHT

GOGO'S EVOLUTION BAR: 10

8. ANGOR

NIGHT MYSTERIES ARE NO SECRET TO ANGOR.

SPECIAL ABILITY: INSOMNIA
FAVOURITE GAME: IN FLIGHT

GOGO'S EVOLUTION BAR: 6

9. TAI-UMU

WITH THE POINTS OF HIS MOUTH-STAR HE CHEWS THE HARDEST THINGS.

SPECIAL ABILITY: STAR SCREAM
FAVOURITE GAME: BOWLING

GOGO'S EVOLUTION BAR: 13

10. KOKU-CHAN

HE MUST GO TO THE BARBER EVERY DAY BECAUSE HIS HAIR GROWS WHILE HE PLAYS.

SPECIAL ABILITY: MANIC HAIR
FAVOURITE GAME: IN FLIGHT

GOGO'S EVOLUTION BAR: 13

11. CHIRU

THE MOON REFLECTS IN HIS EYES WHEN HE'S SLEEPY.

SPECIAL ABILITY: COUNTING SHIP
FAVOURITE GAME: BASKET

GOGO'S EVOLUTION BAR: 8

12. NUCHAN

SERIOUS AND THOUGHTFUL. HE ACTS LIKE THE CHIEF GOGO.

SPECIAL ABILITY: ACTION PLANNING
FAVOURITE GAME: ON LINE

GOGO'S EVOLUTION BAR: 11

13. OM-POH

USES SPELLS TO PLAY BETTER. SOMETIMES IT WORKS.

SPECIAL ABILITY: MULTIPLE FACES
FAVOURITE GAME: BATTLE

GOGO'S EVOLUTION BAR: 10

14. NEBUB

CONCENTRATES THE WATER SUPPLY TO PUT OUT ANY FIRE.

SPECIAL ABILITY: FIREFIGHTING
FAVOURITE GAME: ON LINE

GOGO'S EVOLUTION BAR: 9

15. HAZER

HIS GAME STYLE IS FUNNY AND GOES CRAZY WATCHING OTHERS PLAY.

SPECIAL ABILITY: UNINTENTIONAL HUMOUR
FAVOURITE GAME: BATTLE

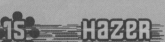

GOGO'S EVOLUTION BAR: 11

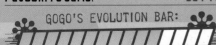

16. SUNON

TICKLISH ALL OVER HIS BODY. NOBODY CAN EVER STAND CLOSE TO HIM.

SPECIAL ABILITY: TICKLISH
FAVOURITE GAME: BATTLE

GOGO'S EVOLUTION BAR: 12

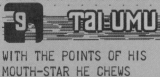

17 HIROKI

NEVER AFRAID OF NEW GAMES.
ALWAYS ON THE FRONT LINE.

SPECIAL ABILITY: BRAVERY
FAVOURITE GAME: ON LINE

GOGO'S EVOLUTION BAR: 14

18 AKONE

THE MASTERS MADE HIM
INTO A KUNG FU HERO.

SPECIAL ABILITY: INVISIBLE KARATE CHOP
FAVOURITE GAME: SCORING

GOGO'S EVOLUTION BAR: 13

19 SULLY

THE ENERGY OF THE
STARS IS ALWAYS WITH HIM...
OR SO HE SAYS.

SPECIAL ABILITY: FORCE CONCENTRATION
FAVOURITE GAME: BASKET

GOGO'S EVOLUTION BAR: 10

20 NARION

HE SHOWS HIMSELF IN
DARKNESS THANKS TO HIS
GLOWING GLASSES.

SPECIAL ABILITY: PARTICLE SEARCHER
FAVOURITE GAME: BATTLE

GOGO'S EVOLUTION BAR: 8

21 SIMSEI

HIS MOUTH ACTS LIKE
A FREEZER AND HE'S
ALWAYS SHIVERING.

SPECIAL ABILITY: WALKING FREEZER
FAVOURITE GAME: BASKET

GOGO'S EVOLUTION BAR: 4

22 DOKI

HE HAS AN INCREDIBLY
SWEET TOOTH.

SPECIAL ABILITY: SWEET GOBBLER
FAVOURITE GAME: BASKET

GOGO'S EVOLUTION BAR: 12

23 HIRCHAN
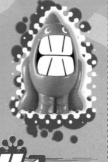

NO HOOK AND NO EYE PATCH
BUT THIS PIRATE IS STILL
SAILING THE HIGH SEAS.

SPECIAL ABILITY: TREASURE FINDER
FAVOURITE GAME: SCORING

GOGO'S EVOLUTION BAR: 5

24 RUFISTAR

HE'S THE MAIN ATTRACTION
AT ANY PARTY. CREATES
FUN FOR EVERYONE.

SPECIAL ABILITY: HELL RAISER
FAVOURITE GAME: BATTLE

GOGO'S EVOLUTION BAR: 11

25 TEMSEI

HE'S A REAL HANDYMAN. HE FIXES ANYTHING...EXCEPT HIS OWN SHOELACES!

SPECIAL ABILITY: FIXER FANTASTIC
FAVOURITE GAME: SCORING

GOGO'S EVOLUTION BAR: **11**

26 PILHY

HE'S GOT A POSITIVE POLE, A NEGATIVE POLE AND HE'S FULLY CHARGED.

SPECIAL ABILITY: ELECTRIC PLAY
FAVOURITE GAME: IN FLIGHT

GOGO'S EVOLUTION BAR: **14**

27 DORO

RESTLESS AND PLAYFUL. HE GETS NERVOUS WHEN NOBODY PLAYS.

SPECIAL ABILITY: VALIANT IDEAS
FAVOURITE GAME: BASKET

GOGO'S EVOLUTION BAR: **10**

28 DANOKI

LOVES TO LURK AROUND CORNERS AND HIDE FROM OTHERS.

SPECIAL ABILITY: CAMOUFLAGE
FAVOURITE GAME: IN FLIGHT

GOGO'S EVOLUTION BAR: **12**

29 MC MASK

HIS HEAD IS ALWAYS IN THE CLOUDS. HE'S A DREAMER.

SPECIAL ABILITY: IMAGINATION
FAVOURITE GAME: ON LINE

GOGO'S EVOLUTION BAR: **9**

30 GAISOR

FIRM AND FAIR. HE LIKES TO BE IN COMMAND OF EVERY SITUATION

SPECIAL ABILITY: LASER ORDER
FAVOURITE GAME: BATTLE

GOGO'S EVOLUTION BAR: **10**

31 LESSEI

MOVES HIS HEAD TO THE RHYTHM OF ANY MUSIC.

SPECIAL ABILITY: ROTATING NECK
FAVOURITE GAME: K.O.

GOGO'S EVOLUTION BAR: **15**

32 POPO

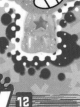

DOESN'T LIKE TOO MANY BUMPS BUT, WITH HIS LUCKY STAR, HE IS A VERY SKILFUL PLAYER.

SPECIAL ABILITY: LUCKY STAR
FAVOURITE GAME: BOWLING

GOGO'S EVOLUTION BAR: **12**

33 IMOOKI

A VOICE IN HIS EARPHONES TELLS HIM THE RULES OF EVERY GAME. HE'S GOT SUCH A TERRIBLE MEMORY.

SPECIAL ABILITY: VOICE RECORDER
FAVOURITE GAME: BASKET

GOGO'S EVOLUTION BAR: 11

34 JEZO

A LONG LOSING STREAK HAS MADE THIS ONCE CONFIDENT GOGO SUDDENLY VERY MODEST.

SPECIAL ABILITY: MACROMODESTY
FAVOURITE GAME: BATTLE

GOGO'S EVOLUTION BAR: 6

35 SUMI

FULL OF ENCOURAGEMENT, SUMI WELCOMES EVERYONE WITH OPEN ARMS.

SPECIAL ABILITY: HUGS
FAVOURITE GAME: SCORING

GOGO'S EVOLUTION BAR: 13

36 SHOON

EVOLUTION MADE HIM SAFETY CONSCIOUS. HE LIKES TO SLOW EVERYONE DOWN.

SPECIAL ABILITY: SPEED BUMPS
FAVOURITE GAME: ON LINE

GOGO'S EVOLUTION BAR: 10

37 SUNOK

OPTIMISTIC, HAPPY AND CALM. EVERYTHING IN HIS LIFE IS ABSOLUTELY OK.

SPECIAL ABILITY: POSITIVITY
FAVOURITE GAME: BOWLING

GOGO'S EVOLUTION BAR: 8

38 FIZER

ALWAYS READY TO GET THE GAME STARTED.

SPECIAL ABILITY:
ULTIMATE COUNTDOWN
FAVOURITE GAME: BASKET

GOGO'S EVOLUTION BAR: 7

39 GAR-GAR

FOUNDER OF THE GOGO'S AEROSPACE ASSOCIATION. ALWAYS SEARCHING FOR NEW HORIZONS.

SPECIAL ABILITY: GALACTIC TOURIST
FAVOURITE GAME: BASKET

GOGO'S EVOLUTION BAR: 12

40 HAYORI

EVOLUTION HASN'T CHANGED HER VANITY. HER HAIR MUST ALWAYS BE PERFECT.

SPECIAL ABILITY: HAIR STYLING
FAVOURITE GAME: BASKET

GOGO'S EVOLUTION BAR: 4

41 MIGU

THE TOUGH GUY IN THE
TROOP. HE CAN THROW A GOGO
HIGHER THAN ANYONE ELSE.

SPECIAL ABILITY: OBJECT THROWER
FAVOURITE GAME: K.O.

GOGO'S EVOLUTION BAR: 8

42 JITTY

KEEPS HIMSELF COOL BY
FLAPPING HIS BIG EARS.

SPECIAL ABILITY: COOLING EARS
FAVOURITE GAME: IN FLIGHT

GOGO'S EVOLUTION BAR: 11

43 VELOP

HE CAN MEASURE HIS
SPEED AND THAT OF ANY
APPROACHING GOGO.

SPECIAL ABILITY: SPEED GUN
FAVOURITE GAME: ON LINE

GOGO'S EVOLUTION BAR: 9

44 TRIKE

VERY HAPPY WITH HIS
EVOLUTION, HE HAS GREAT
PRIDE IN HIMSELF.

SPECIAL ABILITY: CRUSHING HANDS
FAVOURITE GAME: BATTLE

GOGO'S EVOLUTION BAR: 10

45 BOKI

A BIG TUMMY AND BIG APPETITE.
THIS IS ONE GOGO WHO IS
ALWAYS IN TIME FOR A MEAL.

SPECIAL ABILITY: POTBELLIED PUNCTUALITY
FAVOURITE GAME: BASKET

GOGO'S EVOLUTION BAR: 10

46 CHIMU

NEVER AFRAID TO GET
HURT. THIS IS ONE GOGO
WHO IS READY FOR ANY
DARING CHALLENGE.

SPECIAL ABILITY: RUBBER STOP
FAVOURITE GAME: ON LINE

GOGO'S EVOLUTION BAR:  6

47 DUOP

A REAL SPLIT PERSONALITY.
YOU'D BETTER BE CAREFUL
WITH HOW MUCH YOU TRUST HIM.

SPECIAL ABILITY: TWO-FACE
FAVOURITE GAME: BOWLING

GOGO'S EVOLUTION BAR: 5

48 TUBOR

ALWAYS ALERT AND ALWAYS
AWARE. HIS SENSES ARE EVEN
HIGHER WHEN HE SLEEPS.

SPECIAL ABILITY: HYPER ATTENTION
FAVOURITE GAME: ON LINE

GOGO'S EVOLUTION BAR:  7

PHOTO TIME!

EVERYONE, WE HAVE A GROUP PRESENT THIS YEAR...

YOU'RE GONNA LOVE THIS... GUYS, BRING IT IN!

FACT MATCH!

HAS AN EXCELLENT SENSE OF SMELL **10**

3 DISAPPEARS UNDERWATER FOR LONG PERIODS OF TIME.

TAKI

VELOP

HAYORI

7

THE GOGO HANDYMAN

5 PRIDES HERSELF ON HAVING PERFECT HAIR

TEMSEI

4 CAN MEASURE THE SPEED OF OTHER GOGO'S

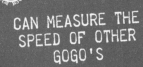

SHOON

SERIES TWO GOGO'S ARE THE EVOLUTIONS, BUT HOW WELL
DO YOU KNOW THEM? WE'VE MIXED UP FACTS FOR TEN GOGO'S,
SEE IF YOU CAN MATCH THEM TO THE RIGHT GOGO!

2 HAS A STAR-SHAPED MOUTH

SNOK

9 LISTENS TO LOUD MUSIC

TAI-UMU

8 A SAFETY CONSCIOUS GOGO

6 A SAFETY CONSCIOUS GOGO

KAM

AKONE

VATCO

1 KNOWN AS A KUNG FU HERO

1	6 ....
2	7 ....
3	8 ....
4	9 ....
5	10 ....

43

49 CUPIH

USES HIS SCREEN-FACE
TO PLAY GOGO GAMES
WITH HIS FRIENDS.

SPECIAL ABILITY: GAME PLAYER
FAVOURITE GAME: H.O.

GOGO'S EVOLUTION BAR: 8

50 B-KORI

HE'S SO FRIENDLY THAT HIS
HORNS DON'T SCARE ANYBODY.

SPECIAL ABILITY: MAKES FRIENDS
FAVOURITE GAME: BATTLE

GOGO'S EVOLUTION BAR: 7

51 CROOKI

AN ELECTRIC SHOCK HAS
LEFT HIM FULLY CHARGED.

SPECIAL ABILITY: ELECTRO SMILE
FAVOURITE GAME: SCORING

GOGO'S EVOLUTION BAR: 6

52 FUSO

A WILD DANCER. HE MAKES
MOVES THAT OTHERS
COULDN'T EVEN IMAGINE.

SPECIAL ABILITY: MUSIC FEVER
FAVOURITE GAME: SCORING

GOGO'S EVOLUTION BAR: 6

53 EGOR

THE HUNGRIEST GOGO OF ALL.
KEEPS HIS MOUTH WIDE OPEN
FOR INSTANT SNACKING.

SPECIAL ABILITY: ULTIMATE EATING
FAVOURITE GAME: BASKET

GOGO'S EVOLUTION BAR: 7

54 TARI

NEVER PLAY HIDE AND
SEEK WITH TARI. HE
WINS EVERY TIME.

SPECIAL ABILITY: BIONIC EYE
FAVOURITE GAME: H.O.

GOGO'S EVOLUTION BAR: 9

55 E-FLO

THIS GOGO LOVES
NATURE, WILDLIFE AND
OUTDOOR ADVENTURES.

SPECIAL ABILITY: EXPLORATION
FAVOURITE GAME: H.O.

GOGO'S EVOLUTION BAR: 10

56 BALU

HE'S FASCINATED BY
HEAD-TO-HEAD CHALLENGES.
A REAL THRILL SEEKER.

SPECIAL ABILITY: EXPLOSIVE RIVALRY
FAVOURITE GAME: BASKET

GOGO'S EVOLUTION BAR: 6

57 YONOZI

LIKES TO GET EVERYTHING
ARRANGED IN PERFECT
DETAIL. EVERY DETAIL
IS DOUBLE CHECKED.

SPECIAL ABILITY: ORGANISATION
FAVOURITE GAME: BATTLE

GOGO'S EVOLUTION BAR: 8

58 EKEN

HE'S GOT AN ANTI-BUMP
POSITION WHICH MAKES HIM
EXTRA HARD TO TUMBLE DOWN.

SPECIAL ABILITY: SOLID STANCE
FAVOURITE GAME: BASKET

GOGO'S EVOLUTION BAR: 7

59 KALIN

AN IMPORTANT GOGO WHO
CARRIES NEWS AND INFORMATION
TO THE OTHERS.

SPECIAL ABILITY: GOGO'S REPRESENTATIVE
FAVOURITE GAME: IN FLIGHT

GOGO'S EVOLUTION BAR: 6

60 KINGO

A BODY THAT LOOKS LIKE A
FACE, A FACE THAT LOOKS LIKE
A BODY..SOME GOGO'S DON'T
KNOW WHAT TO MAKE OF HIM.

SPECIAL ABILITY: BODY-FACE
FAVOURITE GAME: BATTLE

GOGO'S EVOLUTION BAR: 13

61 FAWA

THE OFFICIAL PHOTOGRAPHER.
ALWAYS READY TO CAPTURE
A KEY MOMENT.

SPECIAL ABILITY: PHOTOGRAPHIC VISION
FAVOURITE GAME: K.O.

GOGO'S EVOLUTION BAR: 6

62 FANTU
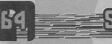

WHEN IT'S TIME FOR HIM TO
PLAY, HE'S SO HAPPY THAT
HIS EYE STARTS DANCING.

SPECIAL ABILITY: RESTLESS EYE
FAVOURITE GAME: BASKET

GOGO'S EVOLUTION BAR: 3

63 TUCOR

A SORE LOSER BUT REALLY
HE HAS A KIND HEART.

SPECIAL ABILITY: GRUMPY SMILES
FAVOURITE GAME: K.O.

GOGO'S EVOLUTION BAR: 8

64 SUT

SOMETIMES HE WALKS
LIKE A ZOMBIE. SLEEPING
PROBLEMS MAYBE?

SPECIAL ABILITY: ZOMBIE TRANCE
FAVOURITE GAME: IN FLIGHT

GOGO'S EVOLUTION BAR: 9

65 TAKI

COVERS HIS EYES TO TRAIN HIS SENSE OF SMELL. HE IS ALWAYS RIGHT.

SPECIAL ABILITY: CANINE SENSE OF SMELL
FAVOURITE GAME: ON LINE

GOGO'S EVOLUTION BAR: 10

66 SHIMY

HE JUST WANTS TO PLAY GAMES ALL DAY LONG. NEVER TOO TIRED TO PLAY.

SPECIAL ABILITY: HAPPY SMILE
FAVOURITE GAME: K.O.

GOGO'S EVOLUTION BAR: 14

67 KAM

OBSESSED WITH MUSIC. TALK LOUDLY IF YOU WANT HIS ATTENTION.

SPECIAL ABILITY: MUSICAL EAR
FAVOURITE GAME: ON LINE

GOGO'S EVOLUTION BAR: 7

68 FLICK

IT'S IMPOSSIBLE TO KNOCK HIM DOWN IF YOU LOOK STRAIGHT INTO HIS EYES.

SPECIAL ABILITY: HYPNOSIS
FAVOURITE GAME: IN FLIGHT

GOGO'S EVOLUTION BAR: 9

69 SIP

LOOKS LIKE HE HAS BAD EYESIGHT BUT HIS AIM IS PERFECT EVERY TIME.

SPECIAL ABILITY: HITTING THE TARGET
FAVOURITE GAME: BOWLING

GOGO'S EVOLUTION BAR: 6

70 TRIKU

PAYS GOOD ATTENTION TO THE GAME... FROM THE FRONT, LEFT AND RIGHT.

SPECIAL ABILITY: TRIPLE VISION
FAVOURITE GAME: BOWLING

GOGO'S EVOLUTION BAR: 7

71 MIZU

LOCKS THE TARGET WITH HIS EYES AND FIRES STRAIGHT DOWN THE MIDDLE.

SPECIAL ABILITY: MIZU STRAIGHT THROW
FAVOURITE GAME: ON LINE

GOGO'S EVOLUTION BAR: 7

72 VATCO

WANTS TO EAT SOMETHING, BUT DOESN'T KNOW WHAT.

SPECIAL ABILITY: UNKNOWN APPETITE
FAVOURITE GAME: BATTLE

GOGO'S EVOLUTION BAR: 10

73 MAKA

A TRUE INDIVIDUAL. HAPPY WITH HIS UNUSUAL LOOKS.

SPECIAL ABILITY: PAINTS CLOUDS
FAVOURITE GAME: SCORING

GOGO'S EVOLUTION BAR: 14

74 FEMO

HE CAN'T WAIT TO JOIN GAR-GAR'S AEROSPACE ASSOCIATION.

SPECIAL ABILITY: UFO DETECTOR
FAVOURITE GAME: SCORING

GOGO'S EVOLUTION BAR: 13

75 CRUSER

PERFORMS GREAT MAGIC TRICKS, EVEN THOUGH HE CAN'T HIDE ANYTHING.

SPECIAL ABILITY: TRANSPARENT MAGIC TRICKS
FAVOURITE GAME: SCORING

GOGO'S EVOLUTION BAR: 8

76 MISORI

LACKING IN CONFIDENCE BUT ALWAYS PLAYS BETTER THAN EXPECTED.

SPECIAL ABILITY: EAR ANTENNA
FAVOURITE GAME: SCORING

GOGO'S EVOLUTION BAR: 9

77 ZUY

HE THINKS THAT HE'LL WIN EVERY GAME..UNFORTUNATELY HE SUFFERS A LOT OF DISAPPOINTMENT.

SPECIAL ABILITY: WINNING SPIRIT
FAVOURITE GAME: K.O.

GOGO'S EVOLUTION BAR: 11

78 TIN-CHU

ALWAYS PROPOSING SOME FOUL PLAY. LOVES WRESTLING.

SPECIAL ABILITY: TIN-CHU CHOP
FAVOURITE GAME: BATTLE

GOGO'S EVOLUTION BAR: 6

79 SNOK

SPENDS LONG HOURS UNDER WATER. EVERYBODY GOES CRAZY LOOKING FOR HIM.

SPECIAL ABILITY: DEEP BREATHING
FAVOURITE GAME: BOWLING

GOGO'S EVOLUTION BAR: 12

80 KIVU

CAREFULLY CONCENTRATES HIS THOUGHTS BEFORE ANY ATTACK.

SPECIAL ABILITY: CONCENTRATION
FAVOURITE GAME: IN FLIGHT

GOGO'S EVOLUTION BAR: 11

GOGO'S WORDSEARCH!

CAN YOU FIND THE TEN SERIES TWO GOGO'S THAT ARE HIDDEN IN THE WORDSEARCH BELOW?

Danoki

Vatco

Hayori

P	O	P	K	I	V	O	P
I	I	E	H	L	M	P	D
P	T	S	E	V	A	O	A
I	O	N	L	K	A	P	N
M	R	O	E	R	I	C	O
O	N	A	D	G	E	V	K
H	A	Y	O	V	A	T	U
I	R	O	Y	A	H	H	J
L	A	H	Y	N	N	A	D
L	U	T	S	N	B	K	L
H	I	S	K	O	I	L	T	W
N	O	K	N	S	O	A	D
G	V	Z	O	M	C	O	A
K	D	G	Q	N	T	A	V
R	O	T	E	C	A	R	A
L	B	N	P	I	V	D	T
D	G	A	S	V	A	T	C

Heled

Sip

Kivu

Moshi

Snok

Popo

Racetor

48

FORGETFUL IMOOKI!

IMOOKI IS SO FORGETFUL THAT HE HAS TO RELY ON HIS EARPHONES TO TELL HIM THE RULES OF EVERY GAME!

BUT TODAY HE HAS FORGOTTEN THE NAMES OF SOME OF HIS FRIENDS, AND HIS EARPHONES DON'T HAVE THE ANSWERS — CAN YOU HELP HIM OUT?!

① _I_S_I

② T__-_MU

③ RUF____

④ A_O_E

⑤ _KR

⑥ __Z_R

HOW TO PLAY IN FLIGHT!

A GAME THAT TESTS YOUR SKILL, SPEED AND AGILITY, AS WELL AS THE FLIGHT OF YOUR CHOSEN GOGO, THIS ONE IS A REAL CHALLENGE!

USE THE 'FLYING ZONE' OPPOSITE TO PLAY THE GAME AGAINST YOUR MATES, OR TO PRACTICE FLYING SOLO..!

FIRST, THOUGH, GET THE HANG OF THE GAME BY LEARNING THE RULES.

2
Take the Gogo from the middle and throw it into the air.
So far so good…

1

Each player, in turn, places a Gogo on each of the four corners of the 'flying zone' with a fifth in the middle.

3

…but here comes the tricky part, paying attention?! While your Gogo is in the air, try to pick up each of your other Gogos.

4
Then, before your flying Gogo hits the ground, try to catch it!

5
If you do not catch your flying Gogo, you do not get any points.

6
The player that picks up the most Gogo's wins the game.

FLYING ZONE!!!

BELOW IS OUR CUSTOM-MADE FLYING ZONE FOR YOU TO USE WHEN PLAYING IN FLIGHT.

SIMPLY PUT A GOGO IN EACH OF THE PLACES AND YOU'RE READY TO GO!

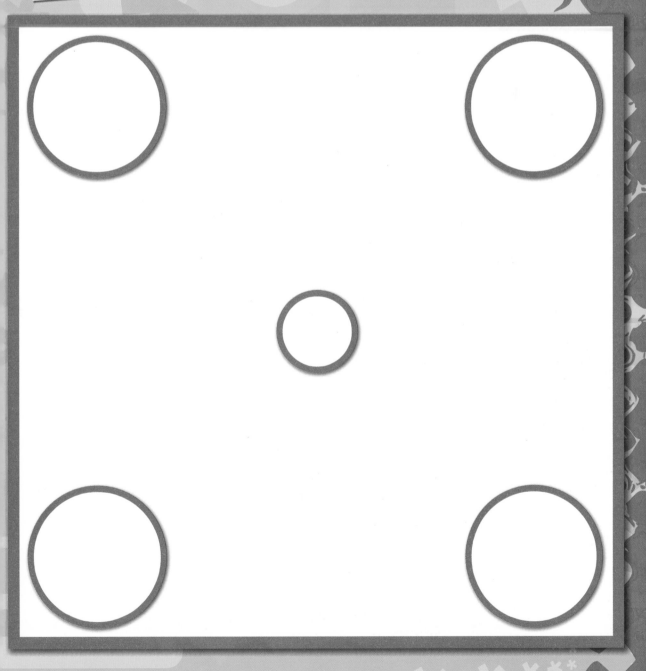

Profiles

1. Flamer

KEEPS THE OTHER GOGO'S WARM, EVEN IN THE COLDEST PLACES.

SPECIAL ABILITY:
CHIMNEY MOUTH

FAVOURITE GAME:
BASKET

HIDES AMONGST THE SHADOWS AND DISCOVERS SECRET PLACES.

SPECIAL ABILITY:
DODGES LOOKS

FAVOURITE GAME:
IN FLIGHT

2. Eydo

KING OF THE VIRTUAL WORLD – CAN MASTER A WHOLE LOAD OF VIDEO GAMES.

SPECIAL ABILITY:
SCREEN JUMPING

FAVOURITE GAME:
SCORING

3. Tivi

4. Xar

GOES UNDER WATER AND HAS THE FISH LAUGHING THEIR HEADS OFF.

SPECIAL ABILITY:
WATER JOKES

FAVOURITE GAME:
ON LINE

5. Raylo

CAN FIND ITS WAY AROUND, EVEN IF IT'S POURING WITH RAIN.

SPECIAL ABILITY:
WALKS THROUGH STORMS

FAVOURITE GAME:
BATTLE

SPEED AND URBAN SPORTS ARE ITS THING. ROLLERS, SKATEBOARDS AND BIKES.

SPECIAL ABILITY:
ROAD RUNNER

FAVOURITE GAME:
BOWLING

6. Tork

ALWAYS DREAMING UP IN THE TREES WITH THE BIRDS, LETTING ITS IMAGINATION FLY.

SPECIAL ABILITY:
BIRDSONG

FAVOURITE GAME:
IN FLIGHT

7. Birtu

8. Mo

NEVER STOPS EATING, BUT ALWAYS KEEPS FIT. JOINS EVERY EXPEDITION.

SPECIAL ABILITY:
ENERGETIC EATING

FAVOURITE GAME:
BOWLING

Profiles

9. Zhip

HAS THE ABILITY TO OPEN JUST ABOUT ANYTHING. A POPULAR COMPANION ON GOGO EXPEDITIONS.

SPECIAL ABILITY: OPENS EVERYTHING

FAVOURITE GAME: SCORING

NEVER AGREES WITH THE ROUTES, BUT ALWAYS TAGS ALONG.

SPECIAL ABILITY: OPPOSITE VIEWS

FAVOURITE GAME: BOWLING

10. Onikaso

LIKELY TO APPEAR SUDDENLY IN THE MOST UNEXPECTED PLACES, LIKE A GHOST.

SPECIAL ABILITY: HAPPY MUSIC

FAVOURITE GAME: SCORING

11. Fanbon

12. Jampa Jampa

CHOOSES UPWARD PATHS, SO THAT IT CAN JUMP ALONG THE ROUTE.

SPECIAL ABILITY: HIGH JUMP

FAVOURITE GAME: BOWLING

13. Lunino

GETS ITS BEARINGS EASILY AS IT HAS ONE EYE ON EACH SIDE. THAT'S A REAL ADVANTAGE.

SPECIAL ABILITY: DOUBLE VISION

FAVOURITE GAME: IN FLIGHT

ALWAYS SEEMS TO PICK THE BEST ROUTES. A LEADER FOR MANY GOGO'S.

SPECIAL ABILITY: SAFE DESTINATION

FAVOURITE GAME: BOWLING

14. Kato

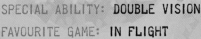

SPECIALISES IN RIVER CROSSINGS, BUT HAS ALSO CROSSED DESERTS. WOW!

SPECIAL ABILITY: SQUARE HEAD

FAVOURITE GAME: SCORING

15. Boox

16. Saileen

DREAMS THAT IT IS A DROP OF WATER THAT HAS EVAPORATED AND IS FLOATING AMONG THE CLOUDS.

SPECIAL ABILITY: FANTASY

FAVOURITE GAME: BOWLING

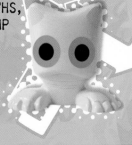

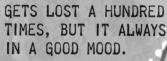

17. Harty

ITS HEART BEATS EACH
TIME IT DISCOVERS
A NEW PLACE.

SPECIAL ABILITY:
ANTENNA HEAD

FAVOURITE GAME:
SCORING

GETS LOST A HUNDRED
TIMES, BUT IT ALWAYS
IN A GOOD MOOD.

SPECIAL ABILITY:
GETS LOST

FAVOURITE GAME:
BOWLING

18. Jaha

THANKS TO ITS SPECIAL
SUIT, IT CAN GO INTO
REALLY HOT CAVES.

SPECIAL ABILITY:
HEAT RESISTANT

FAVOURITE GAME:
BOWLING

19. Shebot

20. Offon

DOESN'T REST OR
STOP, JUST KEEPS
ON GOING.

SPECIAL ABILITY:
EXTRA POWER

FAVOURITE GAME:
SCORING

21. Solfer

IT MAKES UP A SONG
EVERY TIME IT VISITS
A NEW PLACE.

SPECIAL ABILITY:
SONG WRITING

FAVOURITE GAME:
BOWLING

VERY LAID BACK AND A
GOOD HANDYMAN. ABLE
TO REPAIR EVERYTHING.

SPECIAL ABILITY:
KEY MASTER

FAVOURITE GAME:
K.O.

22. Mechi

IF IT DOESN'T WANT
TO BE SEEN, IT TAKES
OFF ITS GLASSES AND
WEARS A MASK.

SPECIAL ABILITY:
CAMOUFLAGE

FAVOURITE GAME:
BASKET

23. Enko

24. Mr. Capi

IF THERE'S A NEW PLACE
TO EXPLORE, IT'S THE
FIRST TO STEP FORWARD.

SPECIAL ABILITY:
DARING DECISIONS

FAVOURITE GAME:
BATTLE

Profiles

25. Amy Nicai

CLOSES ITS EYES SLOWLY AND FLOATS AWAY IN A DREAM.

SPECIAL ABILITY:
DREAMING

FAVOURITE GAME:
IN FLIGHT

NEVER REMEMBERS THE WAY IT CAME, AND HAS TO LOOK FOR THE RETURN ROUTE.

SPECIAL ABILITY:
RANDOM RETURN

FAVOURITE GAME:
BASKET

26. Lostly

SLIDES ALONG REALLY FAST, AND WHEN IT COMES ACROSS AN OBSTACLE, IT HAS TO STOP AND USE ITS AERIAL DRIVE.

SPECIAL ABILITY: K8-DRIVE

FAVOURITE GAME: IN FLIGHT

27. RC-K8

28. Zabrisky

HAS BEEN TRAVELLING FOR A LONG TIME, PARTICULARLY BY TRAIN AND KNOWS ALL THE ROUTES.

SPECIAL ABILITY:
GREAT EXPERIENCE

FAVOURITE GAME: ON LINE

29. Oibel

DIFFERENT FROM ALL THE OTHERS, IT ALWAYS TRAVELS BY CAR AND ALWAYS ARRIVES ON TIME.

SPECIAL ABILITY: PUNCTUALITY

FAVOURITE GAME: BATTLE

OFTEN LOSES THE GROUP AND HAS TO SHOUT LOUDLY TO FIND THEM.

SPECIAL ABILITY:
SHOUTS LOUDLY

FAVOURITE GAME:
BATTLE

30. Swittel

SPENDS SO MUCH TIME IN THE WATER THAT, WHEN IT COMES OUT, IT HAS TO SHOUT "WAIT FOR ME!"

SPECIAL ABILITY:
TALKS TO FISH

FAVOURITE GAME: ON LINE

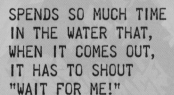

31. Scamy

32. Tar-Tar

TRIES TO AVOID DANGER SO IT CAN KEEP ON GOING AND TRAVEL FAR.

SPECIAL ABILITY:
BRAVERY

FAVOURITE GAME:
BATTLE

Profiles

33. Flycat

BUTTERFLY WIZARD. THE BUTTERFLIES GUIDE IT TO SOME AMAZING PLACES.

SPECIAL ABILITY:
ENCHANTS BUTTERFLIES

FAVOURITE GAME:
IN FLIGHT

LOVES FISH, BUT HATES PUTTING ITS FEET IN THE WATER...EVEN WHEN WEARING BOOTS.

SPECIAL ABILITY:
CAT REFLEXES

FAVOURITE GAME:
ON LINE

34. Fishino

SILENT SOLITARY. ACCOMPANIES THE OTHERS, EVEN THOUGH THEY CAN HARDLY SEE IT.

SPECIAL ABILITY:
MYSTERIOUS SECRET

FAVOURITE GAME:
BATTLE

35. Sarp

36. Lasly

LOVES THE SMALL DETAILS IN EVERY PLACE.

SPECIAL ABILITY:
ROMANTIC EXPLORER

FAVOURITE GAME:
K.O.

37. Lups

RUNS AROUND EVERYWHERE. IS REALLY FAST AND CAN SNIFF OUT EVEN THE MOST DIFFICULT TRACK TO FOLLOW.

SPECIAL ABILITY:
SNIFT SENSE OF SMELL

FAVOURITE GAME: ON LINE

LIKES TO BE THE BIGGEST GOGO, SO THAT IT CAN TAKE GIANT STRIDES.

SPECIAL ABILITY:
EATS PEANUTS

FAVOURITE GAME:
BASKET

38. Dumdum

ALTHOUGH IT FLIES,IT LOVES LEAVING FOOTPRINTS EVERYWHERE IT GOES.

SPECIAL ABILITY:
LEAVES FOOTPRINTS

FAVOURITE GAME:
IN FLIGHT

39. Giro

40. Artix

TRAVELS TO ART MUSEUMS AND PLAYS AS A STANDING STATUE SO THAT VISITORS LOOK AT IT.

SPECIAL ABILITY:
JOKE ARTIST

FAVOURITE GAME:
ON LINE

41. Uzzle

FITS IN EVERYWHERE AND IS MISSED WHEN IT'S NOT AROUND.

SPECIAL ABILITY:
PUZZLE CRACKER

FAVOURITE GAME:
IN FLIGHT

BIG AND STRONG, BUT ITS SLIPPERY BODY CAN SLIP THROUGH SMALL SPACES.

SPECIAL ABILITY:
STRONG ARM

FAVOURITE GAME:
K.O.

42. Gor

ALTHOUGH IT'S SCARED OF EXPLORING IN THE DARK, IT CAN SEE BETTER AT NIGHT.

SPECIAL ABILITY:
NIGHT EXPLORER

FAVOURITE GAME:
K.O.

43. Starfu

44. Lampetti

LONG-LASTING AND LOW-CONSUMPTION LIGHT. THE IDEAL COMPANION FOR INSPECTING DARK PLACES.

SPECIAL ABILITY:
BRIGHT LIGHT

FAVOURITE GAME: BOWLING

45. Chenko

WALKS FIRMLY AND STEADILY, AT A GOOD PACE.

SPECIAL ABILITY:
CHENKO MARCH

FAVOURITE GAME:
BATTLE

REMEMBERS THOUSANDS OF PLACES, BUT FINDS IT HARD TO LOCATE THEM.

SPECIAL ABILITY:
EXPLORER MEMORY

FAVOURITE GAME:
SCORING

46. Eitor

LIKES TO PLAY JOKES ON OTHERS, BUT DOESN'T GO TOO FAR.

SPECIAL ABILITY:
SUBTLE JOKER

FAVOURITE GAME:
SCORING

47. Moky

48. Hilbo

ALWAYS ADVISES HIS FRIENDS TO HAVE A GOOD BREAKFAST BEFORE SETTING OUT TO EXPLORE.

SPECIAL ABILITY:
COOKIE CRAVINGS

FAVOURITE GAME:
IN FLIGHT

59

GOGO QUIZ!

1. WHICH GOGO'S SPECIAL ABILITY IS 'PUZZLE CRACKER'?

2. KICHI LOVES TO SUCK SWEETS, BUT WHAT COLOUR IS ITS OUTFIT?

3. WHAT IS TARGY'S SPECIAL ABILITY?

4. WHICH GOGO HAS AN ALMOST IMPOSSIBLE TO CRACK EXPLORATION CODE ON ITS HEAD?

5. A ROBOT THAT DOES GYMNASTICS.. WHO IS THIS?

6. IF YOU NEEDED HELP ON A VIDEOGAME, WHO WOULD BE THE BEST GOGO TO ASK?

7. WHICH GOGO HAS AN EYE ON EACH SIDE OF ITS HEAD?

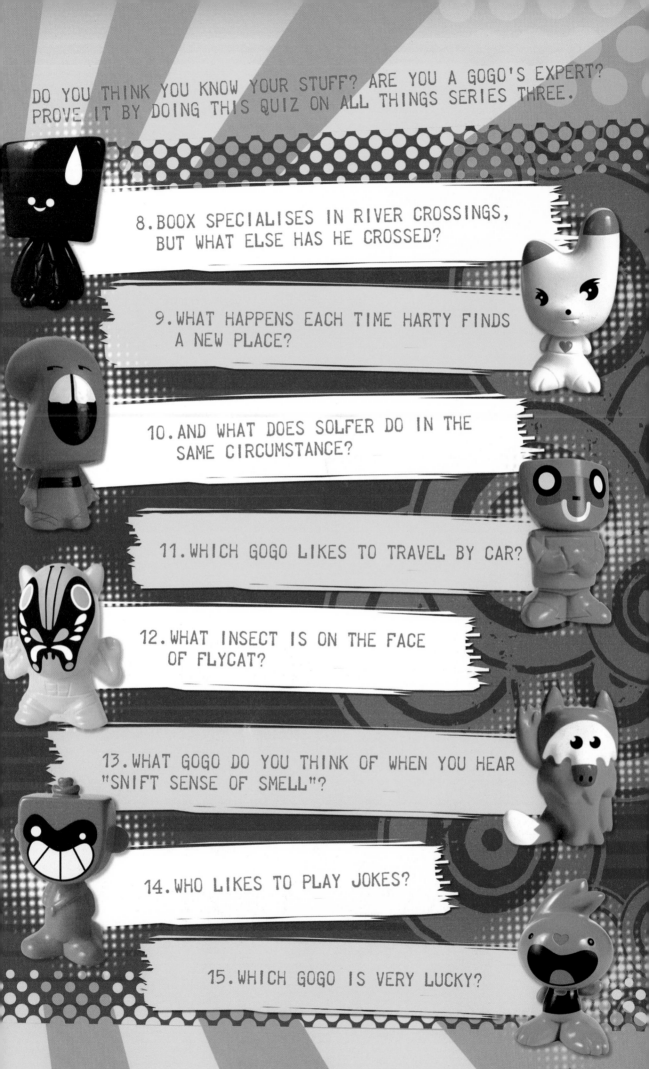

8. BOOX SPECIALISES IN RIVER CROSSINGS,
BUT WHAT ELSE HAS HE CROSSED?

9. WHAT HAPPENS EACH TIME HARTY FINDS
A NEW PLACE?

10. AND WHAT DOES SOLFER DO IN THE
SAME CIRCUMSTANCE?

11. WHICH GOGO LIKES TO TRAVEL BY CAR?

12. WHAT INSECT IS ON THE FACE
OF FLYCAT?

13. WHAT GOGO DO YOU THINK OF WHEN YOU HEAR
"SNIFT SENSE OF SMELL"?

14. WHO LIKES TO PLAY JOKES?

15. WHICH GOGO IS VERY LUCKY?

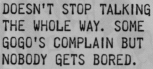
 49. Din-Awa

IS ALWAYS EXCITED,
WHEREVER IT GOES.

SPECIAL ABILITY:
HAPPY ROUTE

FAVOURITE GAME:
BATTLE

DOESN'T STOP TALKING
THE WHOLE WAY. SOME
GOGO'S COMPLAIN BUT
NOBODY GETS BORED.

SPECIAL ABILITY:
BREAKS THE SILENCE

FAVOURITE GAME:
BASKET

50. Chatt

WANTS TO TOUCH EVERYTHING,
AND WHEN IT REACHES A NEW
PLACE, IT STARTS
TO CLAP.

SPECIAL ABILITY:
QUICK HANDS

FAVOURITE GAME:
ON LINE

51. Clappy

52. Lucky Rub

MAYBE IT'S JUST LUCK, BUT
THIS GOGO NEVER HAS ANY
PROBLEMS AND EVERYTHING
ALWAYS GOES WELL.

SPECIAL ABILITY:
VERY LUCKY

FAVOURITE GAME: ON LINE

53. Whas

ADVISES OTHER GOGO'S
WHEN THERE IS ANY
DANGER OR WHEN IT
SEES SOMETHING
INTERESTING
TO EXPLORE.

SPECIAL ABILITY:
DETECTS SURPRISES

FAVOURITE GAME: BASKET

LOVES SWEETS. IF IT
FINDS ONE, IT FORGETS
ABOUT EVERYTHING ELSE.

SPECIAL ABILITY:
SUCKS SWEETS

FAVOURITE GAME:
SCORING

54. Kichi

CAN BE SEEN EASILY
FROM FAR PLACES,
AND CAN BE FOLLOWED
FROM FAR AWAY.

SPECIAL ABILITY:
GUIDING STAR

FAVOURITE GAME:
ON LINE

55. Starboro

56. Zatocat

HAS A SPECIAL SENSE
FOR DETECTING ANY
DANGER AHEAD.

SPECIAL ABILITY:
DETECTS DANGER

FAVOURITE GAME:
ON LINE

Profiles

57. Mori

VERY STRONG WHEN SEATED, AND HAS ALREADY SAVED SEVERAL GOGO'S FROM TROUBLE.

SPECIAL ABILITY: GROUND STRENGTH

FAVOURITE GAME: BASKET

LOVES FINDING PLACES WHERE IT CAN REST QUIETLY.

SPECIAL ABILITY: WINKING EYE

FAVOURITE GAME: K.O.

58. Yimo

NOBODY KNOWS WHERE IT COMES FROM, BUT IT IS ALWAYS KEEN TO JOIN EVERY ADVENTURE.

SPECIAL ABILITY: APPEARS SUDDENLY

FAVOURITE GAME: IN FLIGHT

59. Unfor

60. Comco

ONE OF TIVI'S GOOD FRIENDS. THEY SPEND THE WHOLE DAY PLAYING TOGETHER.

SPECIAL ABILITY: TESTS GAMES

FAVOURITE GAME: K.O.

61. Doc Spavilander

AFTER YEARS OF SEARCHING, IT HAS FOUND ITS FAVOURITE EXPLORATION SITE: THE LABORATORY.

SPECIAL ABILITY: INVESTIGATION

FAVOURITE GAME: BASKET

LIKES TO GET TO THE FRONT OF THE QUEUE AND GIVE THE OTHER GOGO'S SOMETHING TO AIM FOR.

SPECIAL ABILITY: EASY TARGET

FAVOURITE GAME: BASKET

62. Targy

LOVES GETTING LOST IN THE CORNER OF THE FOREST.

SPECIAL ABILITY: MUSHROOM CAMOUFLAGE

FAVOURITE GAME: BOWLING

63. Champler

64. Block

IF EITOR SENDS IT CORRECT INFORMATION, IT CAN FIND ANYTHING STRAIGHT AWAY.

SPECIAL ABILITY: LOCATION GLASSES

FAVOURITE GAME: SCORING

65. Jowa

VERY CARING. POPULAR WITH EVERYONE.

SPECIAL ABILITY:
CARING

FAVOURITE GAME:
BASKET

A BIT OF AN URBAN HOOLIGAN. EVEN BETTER AT SKATING THAN TORK.

SPECIAL ABILITY:
SKATEBOARDING

FAVOURITE GAME:
IN FLIGHT

66. Divel

ALWAYS GOES TO THE MOST CURIOUS AND AMAZING PLACES.

SPECIAL ABILITY:
BOARD GAMES

FAVOURITE GAME:
SCORING

67. Doot

68. Numbar

HAS AN EXPLORATION CODE THAT HARDLY ANYONE CAN BREAK.

SPECIAL ABILITY:
KEY CODE

FAVOURITE GAME:
BASKET

69. Jato

IF THE ROUTE IS A STRAIGHT LINE, THIS GOGO IS THE BEST.

SPECIAL ABILITY:
RUNS IN STRAIGHT LINES

FAVOURITE GAME:
BATTLE

A LITTLE BIT STRANGE BECAUSE, ALTHOUGH IT GETS SEASICK, IT LOVES TRAVELLING BY BOAT.

SPECIAL ABILITY:
GETS SEASICK

FAVOURITE GAME:
K.O.

70. Wolo

LOVES CLIMBING AND FINDS FLAT GROUND REALLY BORING.

SPECIAL ABILITY:
WALL CLIMBING

FAVOURITE GAME:
K.O.

71. Linjat

72. Vladisfor

HAS MORE EXPERIENCE THAN ZABRISKY AND IS CLEVERER THAN DOC PAVILANDER, BUT SPECIALISES IN GROWING VEGETABLES.

SPECIAL ABILITY: PLANTS LETTUCES

FAVOURITE GAME: ON LINE

73. Mobot

VERY WELL PRESERVED
ROBOT THAT ALSO
DOES GYMNASTICS.

SPECIAL ABILITY:
DOES NOT RUST

FAVOURITE GAME:
BATTLE

SEEMS INCREDIBLE,
BUT MANY GOGO'S
DON'T KNOW IF IT HAS
THREE EYES OR ONE.

SPECIAL ABILITY:
SECRET EYES

FAVOURITE GAME:
BATTLE

74: Yucam

TOUCHES ITS TUMMY
TO MEMORISE A PLACE
SO THAT IT CAN FIND
IT AGAIN LATER.

SPECIAL ABILITY:
GPS TUMMY

FAVOURITE GAME:
BOWLING

75. Dori Midori

76. Gondo

BY WHISTLING AND
ORIENTATING ITS SENSITIVE
EARS, IT CAN SENSE IF
THERE IS ANY
WATER NEARBY.

SPECIAL ABILITY:
GENTLE WHISTLE

FAVOURITE GAME: K.O.

77. Min

CAN HYPNOTISE A GOGO
TO STOP IT FROM
FEELING SCARED AND TO
GIVE IT MORE ENERGY.

SPECIAL ABILITY:
HYPNOTIC REPAIR

FAVOURITE GAME: IN FLIGHT

CONCENTRATES A LOT
AND IS VERY QUIET.
IF IT EVER SAYS
ANYTHING, EVERYONE
LISTENS, BECAUSE IT IS
ALWAYS RIGHT.

SPECIAL ABILITY: MENTAL TRUTH

FAVOURITE GAME: IN FLIGHT

78. Ghostmander

SOMETIMES IT CAN'T
DECIDE BUT SHOUTS
"FORWARD" WITH ITS
SMALL MOUTH.

SPECIAL ABILITY:
INDECISIVE

FAVOURITE GAME:
BOWLING

79. Plux

80. Winflag

LOVES FAST MACHINES
LIKE MOTORBIKES, CARS
OR MOTOR BOATS.

SPECIAL ABILITY:
SPEED RADAR

FAVOURITE GAME:
BATTLE

WHOSE HEAD IS IT ANYWAY?

THESE SERIES THREE GOGO'S COLLIDED WHEN PRACTISING THEIR FLYING, AND NOW THEIR BODY PARTS HAVE BEEN MIXED UP — CAN YOU WORK OUT WHICH HEAD BELONGS TO WHICH BODY?

THERE ARE 15 GOGO'S MIXED UP, MATCH EACH NUMBER TO THE RIGHT LETTER.

HOW TO PLAY BATTLE

GO HEAD-TO-HEAD WITH YOUR FRIENDS TO SEE WHO CAN KEEP COOL IN THE HEAT OF BATTLE.

LEARN THE RULES, AND THEN FACE-OFF AGAINST YOUR OPPONENT. THIS TOWN AIN'T BIG ENOUGH FOR THE BOTH OF YOU...!

1

Place six or more Gogo's in a line, the same distance apart.

2

Your opponent then sets up their line opposite yours, an agreed distance apart.

4

Each player has the same number of throws, which you should decide at the start of the game.

3

With one Gogo, try and knock down the opponent's Gogo's.

5

The winner is decided by whoever knocks down the highest number of their opponent's Gogo's.

68

HOW TO PLAY SCORING

THE ULTIMATE TEST OF A GOGO. SCORING TESTS THE FLIGHT, BOUNCE AND LANDING OF A GOGO, AS WELL AS YOUR ABILITY TO THROW THEM.

THIS ONE MIGHT TAKE A BIT OF PRACTICE TO GET THE HANG OF, SO MAKE SURE YOU LEARN HOW TO PLAY FIRST...

SCORING

1

Each player takes a turn to throw five Gogo's at the same time.

2

How your Gogo's land is what counts here. If it lands standing up, you get the highest score of five points. If your Gogo lands on its side, you get two, while if it lands face up you'll get one. If your Gogo lands face down after your throw, it won't score any points!

 5 POINTS

 2 POINTS

 1 POINTS

 0 POINTS

3

The player with the most points after three throws wins the game, so remember to write down how many points you get each time.

69

1. Powi

WELL CONNECTED AND VERY POPULAR. THIS GOGO IS ALWAYS SENDING MESSAGES TO FRIENDS.

POWER SYMBOL:

2. Hik

EVEN WITH MORE THAN TWENTY SPECIAL FIGHTING MOVES, HIK USES HIS HEAD FIRST.

POWER SYMBOL:

3. Eryu

THIS GOGO IS TRYING TO USE WAR PAINT TO HELP WIN SOME GAMES. COULD IT WORK?

POWER SYMBOL:

4. Cora

CORA CAN HEAR THE MUSIC OF THE SEA AND CAN SING WITH THE MOST PERFECT VOICE.

POWER SYMBOL:

5. Welu

WELU CAN JUMP FROM ONE PLANET TO ANOTHER... PROVIDED HE DOESN'T LOSE HIS MASK.

POWER SYMBOL:

6. Geon

A MEAN FACE AND A SPECIAL HELMET... ALWAYS READY FOR THE WORST.

POWER SYMBOL:

7. Mindok

THE MOST HONOURABLE GOGO OF THEM ALL. MINDOK COULD NEVER CHEAT.

POWER SYMBOL:

8. Sini

HER MYSTERIOUS FACE HIDES A POWER THAT NOBODY HAS EVER DISCOVERED.

POWER SYMBOL:

9. Xiu-Sun

A GOGO WITH
SOLAR POWER? THAT
IS XIU-SUN.

POWER SYMBOL:

10. Horo

ONE, TWO, THREE...
HORO IS GONE! A QUICK
THINKING GOGO.

POWER SYMBOL:

11. Okimo

TRIES TO BE EARLY BUT
ALWAYS ARRIVES LATE.

POWER SYMBOL:

12. Asdarin

EVERYONE KNOWS THAT
ASDARIN CONTROLS A
GREAT MAGICAL MYSTERY.

POWER SYMBOL:

13. Dosk

SCARY TO LOOK AT
BUT UNDERNEATH IS
A HEART OF GOLD.

POWER SYMBOL:

14. Terin

SOMETIMES TERIN THINKS
ALL HIS FRIENDS HAVE
RUN AWAY...BUT THEY ARE
RIGHT IN FRONT OF HIM

POWER SYMBOL:

15. Shod

FIVE SUPER-FAST TEETH
MAKE QUICK WORK OF
EVERY MEAL! NEVER
SHARES FOOD WITH ANYONE.

POWER SYMBOL:

16. Dumiel

A FRIEND TO NATURE
AND ALWAYS TO BE
FOUND EXPLORING
THE FOREST.

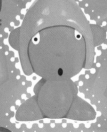

POWER SYMBOL:

17. Reyu

A MASTER AT HIDING LOW DOWN AND POPPING UP TO SURPRISE THE OTHERS.

POWER SYMBOL:

18. Silien

A UNIQUE ROBOT WITH VACUUM POWER. NO CORNER IS LEFT UNTOUCHED.

POWER SYMBOL:

19. Bila

USES SPECIAL ANTENNAE TO DETECT HIDDEN SWEETS.

POWER SYMBOL:

20. Gat

GAT ABSORBS ALL THE HEAT AND ENERGY FROM THE AIR AND RECYCLES IT FOR HIS FRIENDS.

POWER SYMBOL:

21. Moor

WITH HALF A FACE HIDDEN, THIS GOGO ISN'T EASY TO READ. NO ONE LIKES TO GUESS WHAT MOOR IS THINKING.

POWER SYMBOL:

22. Kilo

AN UNUSUAL POWER SURROUNDS KILO, SOMETHING THAT MAKES EVERYONE WANT TO LOOK HIS WAY.

POWER SYMBOL:

23. Wawo

A GOGO SAGE WHO CAN GUIDE THE OTHERS IN IMPORTANT MATTERS.

POWER SYMBOL:

24. Hamo

HAS A REPUTATION FOR BEING MESSY AND DIRTY, BUT IS ACTUALLY OBSESSED WITH BEING CLEAN.

POWER SYMBOL:

Profiles

25. Irgo

A DEMOLITION EXPERT. NOTHING IS AN OBSTACLE.

POWER SYMBOL:

26. Shawa

SHAWA CAN SEE YOUR ANCESTORS WHILST DREAMING. AN INTERESTING GOGO TO KNOW.

POWER SYMBOL:

27. Babu

SHY BABU WILL NEVER PUSH FORWARD TO THE FRONT.

POWER SYMBOL:

28. Jahi

LOVES NOTHING MORE THAN TO WIN BY K.O. THAT'S WHAT THE BUMPER HELMET IS MADE FOR.

POWER SYMBOL:

29. Dak

DAK LISTENS TO MUSIC ALL DAY LONG. HE LOVES TO DANCE!

POWER SYMBOL:

30. Tego

MADE FROM A UNIQUE GOGO ALLOY, TEGO'S BODY CAN BEND IN AN UNUSUAL WAY.

POWER SYMBOL:

31. Din

NOT EASY TO FIND BUT, IF YOU DO, DIN MAY GRANT YOU A WISH.

POWER SYMBOL:

32. Fichup

A SALSA-DANCING EXPERT WHO JUST LOVES TO SHAKE HIS BONES.

POWER SYMBOL:

73

Profiles

33. Moodel

CUDDLY AND ADORABLE, EVERYONE WANTS TO HOLD MOODEL IN THEIR ARMS.

POWER SYMBOL:

34. Garin

THE LIGHT THAT ENTERS THROUGH HIS EYES FILLS HIM WITH ENERGY.

POWER SYMBOL:

35. Fivok

THE ONLY ROBOT WE KNOW WITH A GREAT SENSE OF HUMOUR.

POWER SYMBOL:

36. Kako

AT NIGHT, KAKO CAN MOVE AROUND WITOUT BEING SEEN.

POWER SYMBOL:

37. Flek

FLEK HAS A SMILE THAT INVITES EVERYONE TO PLAY.

POWER SYMBOL:

38. Rita

AFTER ESCAPING FROM A TOP-SECRET LAB, RITA HIDES DAY AND NIGHT, JUST IN CASE...

POWER SYMBOL:

39. Zappi

ANIT-SHOCK ARMOUR AND DIVING SKILLS GIVE THIS GOGO A LOT OF ADVANTAGES.

POWER SYMBOL:

40. Frug

SOMEHOW FRUG IS FIRST AND LAST IN EVERYTHING. NOT EVEN HE KNOWS HOW HE DOES IT!

POWER SYMBOL:

41. Skimo

ABLE TO HANDLE THE
COLDEST CLIMATE
WITH ULTRA-WARM
CLOTHING POWER.

POWER SYMBOL:

42. Yuto

A GOOD FRIEND OF
HIK, HE'S TALLER AND
STRONGER, THOUGH
LESS AGILE.

POWER SYMBOL:

43. Fil Dan

A TERRIFYING LAUGH
MAKES THE OTHER GOGO'S
NERVOUS. SHOULD THEY BE?

POWER SYMBOL:

44. Gulfred

PROBABLY THE HAIRIEST
GOGO OF THEM ALL.
NOBODY FEELS LIKE
COMBING HIM.

POWER SYMBOL:

45. Erhon

PUT ERHON TOGETHER
WITH IRGO AND THEY
COULD SPLIT JUST
ABOUT ANYTHING.

POWER SYMBOL:

46. Belion

THE SUN AND
THE STARS GRANT HIM
A LION'S STRENGTH.

POWER SYMBOL:

47. Eul

BEHIND THESE LOOKS
IS A WEIGHTLIFTING
CHAMPION.

POWER SYMBOL:

48. Uyu

A GIANT EYE THAT CAN
SEE ALL ANGLES. THE
BODY DOESN'T MOVE BUT
THE EYE ROTATES.

POWER SYMBOL:

TAKU WATCHES OVER THE OTHER GOGO'S AT NIGHT, FLYING SILENTLY AMID THE DARKNESS ON THE LOOK-OUT FOR INTRUDERS.

DA-DAH!

WHEEEE!

WHOOPS!

OOMPH!

OH NO...

OOPS

THE END

76

MOST

WANTED

THE GOGO'S THAT EVERYONE WANTS: A HANDFUL OF SUPER RARE AND ULTRA COOL GOGO'S FOR YOU TO COLLECT. THESE GOGO'S HAVE EXTRA SPECIAL DESIGNS, TOO.

YOU CAN TELL WHICH GOGO'S ARE MOST WANTED IN SERIES FOUR AS THEY HAVE '-W' ATTACHED TO THE END OF THEIR NAMES!

THE MOST WANTED GOGO'S FOR SERIES FOUR ARE:

WELU-W   HORO-W   GAT-W   TEGO-W   FRUG-W

HIID-W   GI-HAO-W   DUDA-W   DIRO-W   REIN-W

HORO HURRY!

HORO HAS RACED OFF AHEAD AGAIN, AS USUAL, AND LEFT HIS FRIENDS BEHIND, WONDERING WHERE HE HAS GONE.

THE OTHER GOGO'S DON'T KNOW WHICH WAY HORO WENT, SO CAN YOU FIND A ROUTE FOR THE GROUP TO REACH HORO IN THE MAZE BELOW?

49. Taku

A SKILFUL NIGHT-TIME FLYER WHO WATCHES OVER THE OTHER GOGO'S.

POWER SYMBOL:

50. Hiid

MOVES QUICKLY IN AND OUT OF BUSY TRAFFIC AND KEEPS THINGS MOVING.

POWER SYMBOL:

51. Lim

LIM HAS THE ABILITY TO TURN AN ENEMY INTO A FRIEND WITHIN MOMENTS.

POWER SYMBOL:

52. Lulo

THE ROUNDEST GOGO OF THEM ALL. MOVES WITH SPEED AND SKILL USING PROTECTED EYES.

POWER SYMBOL:

53. Goomi

HE CAN CHANGE THE COLOUR OF HIS BODY, BUT DON'T ASK HIM TO CHANGE HIS T-SHIRT.

POWER SYMBOL:

54. Woki

CONSIDERING HE IS THE KING OF SPIRALS, HE LOOKS FAIRLY HARMLESS.

POWER SYMBOL:

55. Branco

HE IS AS SOLID AS A ROCK. MANY HAVE TRIED TO MOVE HIM AND MANY HAVE FAILED.

POWER SYMBOL:

56. Fusa

A MUSICAL GENIUS WHO CAN CONTROL THE POWER OF ECHOES.

POWER SYMBOL:

57. Forolin

GO HERE, GO THERE, FOROLIN FLIES ANYWHERE.

POWER SYMBOL:

58. Binlod

A MECHANICAL VISUAL SYSTEM ALLOWS HIM TO CALCULATE THE SIZE OF EVERYTHING HE SEES.

POWER SYMBOL:

59. Conrab

BRINGS GOOD LUCK TO ALL THE GOGO'S, JUST AS LONG AS THINGS GO HIS WAY.

POWER SYMBOL:

60. Gi-Kao

GIVES OUT A CRAZY SHRIEK BEFORE EACH STRIKE — GI-KAO!

POWER SYMBOL:

61. Kustor

KUSTOR PLAYS ALL DAY AND RIDES HIS MOTORBIKE ALL NIGHT.

POWER SYMBOL:

62. Urki

HAPPY TO BE A LOYAL PET BUT YOU SHOULD NEVER TIE HIM UP AND LEAVE HIM ALONE.

POWER SYMBOL:

63. Poto

A CIRCUS PROFESSIONAL WHO IS ALWAYS MAKING THE OTHER GOGO'S LAUGH.

POWER SYMBOL:

64. Varin Ray

THE CHIEF OF SECURITY WHENEVER THE POWER GOGO'S GET TOGETHER.

POWER SYMBOL:

65. Vlio

VLIO AND CORA ARE GREAT FRIENDS AND SHARE A LOVE FOR THE SEA.

POWER SYMBOL:

66. Frispiricandy

THE SWEETEST OF GOGO'S AND ONE THAT SENDS BILA'S ANTENNAE CRAZY!

POWER SYMBOL:

67. Guin

A SUPER-COOL GOGO THAT CAN SWIM IN THE COLDEST WATER OF ALL.

POWER SYMBOL:

68. Ilo

IS THIS A GOGO TORTOISE LOOKING FOR A MISSING SHELL?

POWER SYMBOL:

69. Vite

THE SLIGHTEST MOVEMENT IN THE DISTANCE ACTIVATES HIS DETECTION DEVICE.

POWER SYMBOL:

70. Doda

THAT HEAD IS SQUARE FROM WATCHING TOO MUCH TV.

POWER SYMBOL:

71. In-Po

THE GUIDE TO ALL QUESTIONS THAT YOU MAY HAVE ABOUT POWER GOGO'S.

POWER SYMBOL:

72. Ruyt

RUYT CAN GET THINGS A LITTLE CONFUSED SOMETIMES BUT GETS THERE IN THE END.

POWER SYMBOL:

Profiles

73. Tachan

AN APPRENTICE MAGICIAN WHO VERY OFTEN FORGETS TO BRING A WAND.

POWER SYMBOL:

74. Almo

FASHION IS EVERYTHING TO THIS GOGO. NOBODY HAS MORE WARDROBES.

POWER SYMBOL:

75. Diro

STAYS BRIGHT AND HAPPY, EVEN WITHOUT SLEEP FOR THREE DAYS.

POWER SYMBOL:

76. Erendel

CAN OFTEN BE FOUND HIDING IN THE HOLLOW OF A TREE, READY TO SURPRISE DUMIEL.

POWER SYMBOL:

77. Spir

WITH TICKLISH FEET, SPIR WOULD LOVE TO FIND SOME SHOES THAT FIT.

POWER SYMBOL:

78. Fenton

NOT ALL GOGO'S BELIEVE IT, BUT FENTON CAN FLY TO THE MOON.

POWER SYMBOL:

79. Minty

CHANGES COSTUME EACH WEEK. OTHER GOGO'S GUESS WHAT WILL BE NEXT.

POWER SYMBOL:

80. Rein

REIN HAS AN ABILITY TO DETECT SECRET UNDERGROUND WATER SOURCES.

POWER SYMBOL:

CAN YOU REVEAL THE TEN MYSTERY SERIES FOUR GOGO'S IN THE CROSSWORD?

FILL IN THE CROSSWORD TO REVEAL THE NAME OF A HIDDEN GOGO IN THE YELLOW SQUARES!

? erhon

The crossword grid (handwritten answers):

- 1 Down / 1 Across: q u i n
- a
- r
- 4 Across: f i c h u p
- n
- 2 Down: X i
- 3 Across: e u l
- s
- u
- 6 Across: t a c h a n
- 8 Across: D r o
- 7 Down: h a m
- 9 Across: P o w i

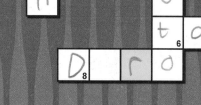

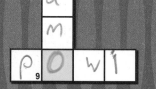

DOWN

1. A Gogo that gains energy through absorbing light with its eye... (5)
2. Which Gogo is solar powered? (6)
5. A circus professional that entertains its friends... (4)
7. Who is obsessed with being clean, but is usually dirty! (4)

ACROSS

1. What Gogo can swim in the coldest water? (4)
3. Who is the Gogo weightlifting champion? (3)
4. Which Gogo loves to dance the salsa? (6)
6. A forgetful magician... (6)
8. Can go days without sleep, which Gogo is this? (4)
9. A popular Gogo, often sending messages to its friends... (4)

SPOT THE DUMIEL DIFFERENCE!

DUMIEL IS A NATURE-LOVER, BUT SOMETHING'S NOT QUITE NATURAL HERE! LOOKING AT THE TWO IMAGES BELOW,

CAN YOU SPOT THE FIVE DIFFERENCES?

HOW TO PLAY BOWLING!

THIS GAME IS ALL ABOUT POWER AND ACCURACY, AS YOU USE YOUR GOGO'S TO TAKE OUT YOUR OPPONENT'S! PICK YOUR GOGO'S WISELY FOR THIS ONE, THEY'LL NEED TO BE ABLE TO FLY WELL BUT ALSO PACK A PUNCH ON IMPACT!

1

Each player must place the same number of Gogo's on the floor, about a hand's width from a wall.

2

Each player takes turns to throw a Gogo, aiming to knock down their opponent's Gogo's.

3

If you knock down one of your own Gogo's on your go, it doesn't matter – just stand it up again, ready for your opponent's throw. You can't do this if you opponent knocks them over, though!

4

The player who knocks all of their opponent's Gogo's over first, wins. Or, you can agree on a number of turns, and the winner that way will be whoever knocks the most Gogo's over.

HOW TO PLAY BASKET!

YOU'LL NEED A STEADY HAND FOR THIS ONE! THIS GAME IS LESS ABOUT POWER AND MORE ABOUT ACCURACY.

USE YOUR BEST FLYING AND BEST BOUNCING GOGO'S FOR BASKET.

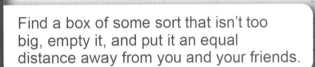

1 Find a box of some sort that isn't too big, empty it, and put it an equal distance away from you and your friends.

2

Take it in turns to try and get your Gogo in the box. It's not as simple as throwing it straight in, though; you have to bounce the Gogo into the box!

3 Each player throws five Gogo's – it is a good idea that they are the same colour, so you can easily tell who has got the most into the basket at the end of the game.

5 Once you've mastered this game, you can challenge yourself by moving the target further away and or making the box smaller!

4 Whoever does get the most Gogo's into the box is the winner.

Profiles

1 MOSH

EVERY GOGO AGREED THAT MOSH SHOULD BE THE NUMBER ONE SUPERSTAR.

2 IMON

IMON HAS ALWAYS DREAMT OF BEING A STAR AND NOW HIS DREAMS HAVE COME TRUE.

3 KATO

THE LEADER OF EVERY EXPEDITION, HE'S A SUPERSTAR WHO IS USED TO BEING FOLLOWED.

9 JELLY

BRAVE JELLY HAS BEEN TRANSFORMED INTO THE ULTIMATE GOGO WARRIOR.

5 SATO

THE UNBEATABLE FIGHTER WITH A K.O. PUNCH THAT HAS NO RIVAL.

6 HIU-SUN

WHAT BETTER SUPERSTAR SUPPORT COULD YOU HAVE THAN THE SUN'S POWER?

7 SHOD

AFTER SCOFFING THE SUPERSTAR CELEBRATION CAKE, SHOD HAD TO ORDER ANOTHER ONE!

8 NASAHO

READY TO USE HIS DOUBLE FAST HOOK TO DEFEND HIS SUPERSTAR TITLE.

Profiles

 9 POWI

MEGA-CONNECTED WITH LOADS OF FRIENDS, POWI GOT PLENTY OF VOTES TO BECOME A SUPERSTAR.

10 MOLLY

KEEPS EVERYONE IN A GOOD MOOD BY TEACHING THEM THE ART OF MICRO-ANGER.

 11 HELLY

AS THE FASTEST GOGO, HELLY HAD TO MAKE THE SUPERSTAR LIST.

12 DAK

ORGANISES GREAT SUPERSTAR PARTIES AND KNOWS JUST HOW TO ENTERTAIN EVERYONE.

 13 LESSEI

HAS NO PROBLEM WITH THE HECTIC SUPERSTAR LIFESTYLE.

14 KOKU-CHAN

CHANGES STYLE SO OFTEN THAT HE SURPRISES ALL THE OTHER SUPERSTARS.

 15 CHENKO

WITH A LIGHT STEP AND DECISIVE MIND, THIS GOGO HAS GONE STRAIGHT TO THE FRONT.

16 IMOOKI

THE SUPERSTAR REPORTER IS ALWAYS ON HAND TO RECORD THE LATEST NEWS.

17 HORO

A QUICK THINKER, WHO CAN MAKE EXTRA-FAST DECISIONS.

18 SHIMY

HAS EVOLVED REALLY WELL, AND SURPRISES EVERYONE WITH A HAPPY SMILE.

19 DORI MIDORI

AN ACE EXPLORER SO EVERYONE TRUSTS HIM.

20 TORI

ALWAYS WORKING ON BIGGER AND BETTER JUMPS, TORI CAN NOW JUMP OVER THE GOGO'S CUBE.

21 DIN-awa

WITH ENTHUSIASM YOU CAN GO FAR! A GOOD ACT TO FOLLOW.

22 MIN

MIN'S HYPNOTISM SHOWS ARE A GREAT HIT WITH THE SUPERSTARS.

23 HARTY

NEARLY MISSED A HEARTBEAT WHEN TOLD ABOUT BEING A SUPERSTAR.

24 TSU

SUPERSTAR TSU'S SOFT DRINKS ARE THE BUSINESS WHEN THE HEAT IS ON.

 25 SIMI

SHOT TO FAME WITH AN AMAZING SMILE.

 26 JAMPA JAMPA

SaMPA JaMPA

LOVES JUMPING FROM ONE GOGO'S CUBE TO ANOTHER.

 27 RACETOR

HIS COMPETITIVE STREAK HAS WON HIM A PLACE AMONG THE SUPERSTARS.

 28 HILBO

READY FOR ANYTHING, AFTER A BIG BREAKFAST OF COURSE.

 29 LUCKY RUB

LUCKY RAB HAD ALL THE LUCK NEEDED TO BECOME A SUPERSTAR. THANKS TO THE HEART SHAPED NOSE PERHAPS?

 30 HIK

A GREAT FIGHTER WHO WAS DESTINED TO BE A SUPERSTAR. HIK ALWAYS USES THE POWER OF WORDS TO AVOID CONFRONTATION.

 31 BOY

DIDN'T WANT TO SEE THE BIG SURPRISE UNTIL IT WAS RIGHT THERE: THE GOGO'S CUBE!

 32 POPO

POPO ALWAYS PLAYS WELL AND GETS PLENTY OF LUCK BUT EVEN AS A SUPERSTAR HE DOESN'T LIKE TO TAKE MANY KNOCKS.

Profiles

  YIMO

EVERYONE LIKES
YIMO'S CUTE WINK.

  AIKO

A SUPERSTAR
SENSE OF SMELL
CAN ALWAYS SNIFF
OUT A PARTY.

 GEON

IF THERE'S TROUBLE
TO BE SOLVED, GEON
IS ALWAYS THERE.

 KICHI

DREAMS OF LIVING
IN A GOGO'S
CUBE MADE OUT
OF CHOCOLATE.

 **MISHA**

POPULAR MISHA
IS NOW ADORED AS
A SUPERSTAR. THE
OTHERS GOGO'S ALWAYS
ASK FOR MISHA HUGS!

FRUG

INSTEAD OF TURNING
INTO A CHICKEN
OR AN OMELETTE,
FRUG HAS BECOME
A SUPERSTAR.

 DIVEL

EVERYONE WANTS THIS
SUPERSTAR-SKATER'S
AUTOGRAPH.

 **ANGIRU**

THE FIRST TO
KNOW THE LIST
OF SUPERSTAR
GOGOS BUT KEPT
THE SECRET SAFE
AS ALWAYS.

 DUMIEL

IN CHARGE OF
TAKING EVERYONE
ON A SUPERSTAR
FIELD TRIP.

 BOKI

BOKI IS NOW SO
FILLED WITH SUCCESS
HE MIGHT NEED TO
GO ON A DIET.

 MAKA

THE SUPERSTAR
EVOLUTION HAS
DONE GREAT THINGS
FOR MAKA. CHECK
OUT THE NEW
COLOURS. WOW!

 FUJICHIK

LANDED ON HIS
FEET IN HIS
SUPERSTAR
GOGO CUBE.

 CHIMU

FANS THROW THEMSELVES
AT SUPERSTAR CHIMU,
BUT THE RUBBER
STOP PROTECTS HIM.

 **RUFISTAR**

HAD THE BRAINS TO
COME UP WITH THE
NAME 'SUPERSTAR'.
EVERYONE'S FAVOURITE!

 SHAWA

IN A DREAM,
AN ANCESTOR SAID
THAT THE FUTURE
WOULD BE BRIGHT.

 RUYT

NOT THE LATEST
TECHNOLOGY BUT
A REALLY FUN
SUPERSTAR ROBOT.

IT IS THE PARTY TO CELEBRATE THE GOGO'S WHO HAVE BECOME SUPERSTARS...

YO!

HERE WE ARE ON THE RED CARPET...

...AND HERE COMES SUPERSTAR SKATER DIVEL!

THERE'S DAK, WHO ORGANISED THIS PARTY!

HI EVERYONE AT HOME!

AND LOOK! IT'S THE FABULOUS MATSUE AND HER WORLD FAMOUS HAIR!

THANK YOU, I DIDN'T EVEN BRUSH IT!

INSIDE, THE SUPERSTARS ARE HAVING A GREAT TIME. THEY'RE...

DANCING!...

EATING!...

PLAYING!...

94

ODD ONE OUT!

SINCE BECOMING SUPERSTARS, THESE GOGO'S HAVE HAD A BIT OF A MAKEOVER. CAN YOU SPOT THE ODD IMAGE OUT OF THE RESTYLED GOGO'S?

SUPERSTAR FASHION!

SUPER-STYLISH DARE WAS ALLOWED TO DESIGN HIS OWN SUPERSTAR COLOURS, BUT HOW WOULD YOU HAVE COLOURED HIM? BELOW ARE IMAGES OF DARE BEFORE AND AFTER HIS STYLE REFRESH AND A BLANK ONE FOR YOU TO GIVE DARE ANOTHER NEW-LOOK!

SUPERSTAR GOGO'S CRAZY BONES

GOGO'S CRAZY BONES

 49 **CORA**

CORA'S PERFECT VOICE IS POPULAR WITH THE SUPERSTARS. THEY ALL LOVE TO HEAR HER SING.

50 **FIST**

A STRONG FIST IN THE AIR TO CELEBRATE BECOMING A SUPERSTAR.

 51 **TERIN**

ALTHOUGH TERIN CAN'T SEE HIS FRIENDS, HE KNOWS THEY ARE ALWAYS WITH HIM.

52 **DUOP**

LOOKS LEFT AND RIGHT WITHOUT MOVING HIS HEAD — THE PERFECT BODYGUARD.

 53 **MC-MASK**

HAD SOME DOUBTS, BUT HIS GREATEST DREAMS HAVE COME TRUE.

54 **CUPIX**

CUPIX ALWAYS PLAYS ONE MORE GAME ON THE FACE-SCREEN BEFORE GOING TO BED.

 55 **DARE**

HE'S SO STYLISH THAT HE WAS ALLOWED TO CHOOSE HIS OWN SUPERSTAR COLOURS.

56 **JAHA**

PUT SOME GOGO'S CUBES TOGETHER AND JAHA WILL BE LOST STRAIGHT AWAY.

 MOOR

MOOR'S TACTICAL
SECRETS ARE A
MYSTERY TO THE
OTHER SUPERSTARS.

 SKIMO

KEEPS EVERYONE
IN A GOOD MOOD
BY TEACHING THEM
THE ART OF
MICRO-ANGER.

 GONDO

GONDO'S WHISTLE
IS VERY USEFUL
FOR CALLING
SUPERSTAR
MEETINGS.

 AKONE

HIS INVISIBLE
KARATE CHOP
CAN KNOCK DOWN
HUGE TOWERS OF
GOGO'S CUBES.

 CROOKI

WITH A GENTLE TOUCH,
THE OTHERS RECEIVE
AN ELECTRIC TICKLE

 JOWA

JOWA AND MISHA
WORK TOGETHER
TO KEEP ALL THE
SUPERSTARS HAPPY.

 MATSUE

MATSUE HAS THE
MOST FAMOUS HAIR
IN THE SERIES,
WHETHER IT'S
BRUSHED OR NOT.

 BRANCO

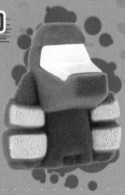

HAS MANAGED TO
GET A PLACE AMONG
THE SUPERSTARS
AND NO-ONE'S
GOING TO MAKE
BRANCO BUDGE.

Profiles

 LIM

HAS ALWAYS MADE FRIENDS WITH HER ENEMIES AND NOW SHE CAN MAKE THE SUPERSTARS HER SUPER-FRIENDS.

 UMU

SINCE BECOMING A SUPERSTAR, UMU COMES OUT OF THE POOL DRY. WOW!

 DIN

AFTER GRANTING SO MANY WISHES, EVERYONE WAS SO GRATEFUL THAT DIN HAD TO BECOME A SUPERSTAR.

 TARGY

THE SUPERSTARS OFTEN USE TARGY AS A MEETING POINT. HE'S JUST SO EASY TO FIND!

 SUNON

AWARDED THE FUNNIEST GOGO MEDAL, BUT DOESN'T WEAR IT BECAUSE IT TICKLES.

 MINTY

BECOMING A SUPERSTAR HAS BEEN MINTY'S MOST RADICAL CHANGE OF CLOTHES.

 DANOKI

IT'S HARD TO HIDE WHEN YOU'RE A SUPERSTAR. EVEN WHEN YOU'VE GOT NEW COLOURS FOR CAMOUFLAGE!

 OJARU

OJARU ALWAYS LIKES TO USE HIS FLYING EARS TO HELP HIM PLACE THE VERY HIGHEST GOGO CUBES.

73 LUNINO

ALWAYS THE FIRST TO SAY HELLO, BECAUSE LUNINO SEES OTHERS BEFORE THEY SEE HIM.

74 JATO

IF YOU WANT TO KNOW THE SHORTEST DISTANCE BETWEEN TWO POINTS, JATO IS THE GOGO TO ASK.

75 DOOT

IS INVINCIBLE AT CHESS AND NOW SPENDS TIME INVENTING NEW GAMES TO PLAY AGAINST THE SUPERSTAR.

76 MORI

SUPERSTAR STRENGTH BUT, AS EVER, MORI NEEDS TO SIT DOWN TO BE MOST EFFECTIVE.

77 RAYLO

WHEN A STORM BREAKS, HE'S THE ONLY ONE THAT DOESN'T RUN AND HIDE IN A GOGO'S CUBE.

78 e-FLO

BRINGS A ROMANTIC TOUCH TO ALL THE SUPERSTARS.

79 DIRO

NEVER GETS TIRED AND IS ALWAYS AWAKE AT THE END OF THE BEST SUPERSTAR PARTIES.

80 SINI

HAS A MYSTERIOUS POWER THAT ATTRACTS EVERYONE'S ATTENTION.

KNOW YOUR

ANGIRU WAS THE FIRST TO KNOW THE IDENTITY OF THE GOGO SUPERSTARS, BUT HOW WELL DO YOU KNOW THIS ELITE BAND OF GOGO'S?

EACH HAS THEIR OWN UNIQUE QUALITY, PASTIME OR PROFESSION, SEE IF YOU CAN CORRECTLY MATCH EACH SUPERSTAR TO THE THING THAT QUALIFIED THEM FOR GOGO STARDOM!

SUPERSTAR ONE:

THIS GOGO IS AN UNBEATABLE FIGHTER, USING THE SUPER-STRONG K.O. PUNCH...

ANSWER.................

SUPERSTAR TWO:

A GOGO THAT KEEPS ITS EAR TO THE GROUND, THIS SUPERSTAR IS RENOWNED FOR THEIR EXPERT NEWS COVERAGE. THE BEST GOGO JOURNALIST AROUND...

ANSWER.................

SUPERSTAR THREE:

BLINK AND YOU'LL MISS IT — THIS GOGO IS THE FASTEST AROUND AND RUSHED STRAIGHT INTO THE LIST OF SUPERSTARS...

ANSWER.................

SUPERSTAR FOUR:

YOU'LL BE IN STITCHES WITH THIS SUPERSTAR; VOTED AS THE FUNNIEST GOGO, THEY'LL HAVE A JOKE UP THEIR SLEEVES FOR YOU...

ANSWER.................

UPERSTARS!

SUPERSTAR FIVE:

THE EXPERT BEHIND THE PERFECT SOFT DRINKS
FOR A SUMMER'S DAY, THIS SUPERSTAR IS AN
EXCELLENT GOGO TO KNOW...

ANSWER.....................

SUPERSTAR SIX:

SOMETHING OF A DAREDEVIL, THIS GOGO IS
AMBITIOUS WITH THEIR JUMPS. SINCE BECOMING
A SUPERSTAR THEY HAVE ALREADY MASTERED
JUMPING OVER THE GOGO'S CUBE!

ANSWER.....................

SUPERSTAR SEVEN:

WHAT'S BETTER THAN A NICE HUG WHEN YOU'RE FEELING
DOWN? AND IF YOU WANT A NICE HUG, THIS SUPERSTAR
IS PERFECT — GIVING ALL THE OTHER GOGO'S HUGS TO
CHEER THEM UP. LOVELY!

ANSWER.....................

SUPERSTAR EIGHT:

ONE OF THE BEST KNOWN IN SERIES FIVE,
THIS GOGO IS A SUPERSTAR-SKATER.
EVERYONE WANTS THEIR AUTOGRAPH!

ANSWER.....................

HOW TO PLAY ON LINE

THIS GAME IS THE ULTIMATE TEST OF YOUR ACCURACY. THROW YOUR GOGO TOO HARD, AND IT'S GAME OVER; DO IT TOO SOFT AND YOU'RE NOT EVEN IN THE GAME!

USE THE 'BATTLE LINE' OPPOSITE TO PLAY ON LINE, HERE ARE THE RULES:

on line

1

2 Use the 'battle line' opposite for this game, placing it an equal distance away from you and your opponent.

2 Each player takes a turn to throw one of their Gogo's, without dragging them.

3

The player that manages to get their Gogo nearest to the line, even if it is behind it, wins the throw.

4 The player that wins the most throws, wins the game. You could do a 'first to five' challenge, the winner being the person who is first to win five throws, or a 'best of ten' – whoever wins the most out of ten throws.

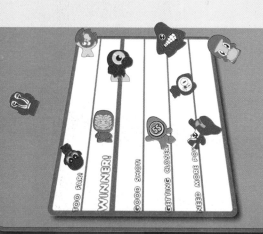

BATTLE LINE!!!

TOO FAR!

WINNER!

GOOD SHOT!

GETTING CLOSER!

NEED MORE POWER!

MOST WANTED

THE BEST OF THE BEST: THESE GOGO'S ARE THE MOST WANTED FROM THE SUPERSTARS SERIES. THERE ARE FOUR MOST WANTED GOGO'S FOR SERIES FIVE, PICKED FROM THE PREVIOUS SERIES.

NOW THEY'VE BECOME SUPERSTARS, THEY'VE GOT A NEW LOOK, TOO!

TAI-UMU

HAS A MEGA METALLIC WAR CRY THAT ALL THE SUPERSTAR GOGO'S RECOGNISE.

HIROKI

HAS NO FEAR AND BECOMING A SUPERSTAR WAS JUST ONE MORE CHALLENGE.

HAZARD

THE BRAVEST AND MOST COURAGEOUS GOGO NOW HAS A SUPERSTAR BITE.

HIRCHAN

THE MOST FAMOUS AND INFAMOUS HAT IN THE SUPERSTAR WORLD. BE WARNED!

GOGO'S MINI GAMES!

WANNA TRY SOMETHING A LITTLE DIFFERENT WITH YOUR GOGO'S? ALREADY MASTERED BASKET OR IN LINE? WANT SOME GAMES YOU CAN PLAY ON YOUR OWN WHILE YOUR FRIENDS ARE EATING THEIR DINNER?

HERE'S A FEW FUN IDEAS TO MIX YOUR GOGO PLAY UP!

FLYING BLIND!

Set up a target – a box, a bag, even a shoe – and stand a fair distance away. Remember where you've set it up, as the next bit is tricky! With the help of a friend or an adult, either put on a blindfold or close your eyes (but no peaking!). Then spin round in a circle five times and try to throw your Gogo into the target. If you can do it first time, you're a pro!

SPIN BOUNCE!

A quick and easy one. Pick your Gogo, bounce it on the floor in front of you and try to spin round and catch it before it bounces for a second time. This tests your speed and your bouncing ability!

GOGO HIGH JUMP!

One for the expert flickers out there. Set up a 'hurdle', using either a box, a book on its side or even two Gogo's on top of each other. Your mission is to flick a Gogo over this target without hitting it! Choose your Gogo carefully!

TARGET TRAINING

Set up five Gogo's in different positions on the floor, near to a wall. Choose yourself a 'shooter' and lie on the floor on the other side of the room. Your mission is to see how many shots it takes to knock all five Gogo's down. If you can do it in five, then you are super accurate!

NEAREST THE GOGO!

Test your accuracy – place a single Gogo in the middle of the floor and stand a long way away from it. Your mission is to roll your other Gogo's to try and get them to land as close to the target as possible (you could use Targy for this one!). This is good for one or two players!

★ ANSWERS

PAGE 15:
EXCLUSIVE SKILLS!

1. Karin
2. Blem
3. Anuik and K-Cul
4. K-Cul
5. Plank

PAGES 24-25: LOST AT SEA!

1. Go left when you see the lighthouse.
2. Then, go straight for about two miles.
3. You will see a deserted beach on your right.
4. Dock your boar here.
5. Dig a hole about 50 metres up the beach.
6. You will find your treasure!

PAGE 48:
GOGO'S WORDSEARCH

P	O	P	K	I	V	O	P
I	I	E	H	L	M	P	D
P	I	S	E	V	A	O	A
I	O	N	L	K	A	P	N
M	R	O	E	R	I	C	O
O	N	A	D	G	E	V	K
H	A	Y	O	V	A	T	U
I	R	O	Y	A	H	H	J
L	A	H	Y	N	N	A	D
L	U	T	S	N	B	K	L
H	I	S	K	O	N	T	W
N	O	K	N	S	O	A	D
G	V	Z	O	M	C	O	A
K	D	G	Q	N	T	A	V
R	O	T	E	C	A	R	A
L	B	N	P	I	V	D	T
D	G	A	S	V	A	T	C

PAGES 30-31:
GOGO'S GO FLYING!

Ojaru jumps furthest.

PAGES 42-43:
FACT MATCH!

1. Snok
2. Shoon
3. Kam
4. Temsei
5. Tai-Umu
6. Taki
7. Vatco
8. Akone
9. Hayori
10. Velop

PAGE 49:
FORGETFUL IMOOKI!

1. Sker
2. Tai-Umu
3. Hazer
4. Akone
5. Simsei
6. Rufstar

ANSWERS ☆

PAGES 60-61: GOGO QUIZ!

1. Uzzle
2. Yellow
3. Easy Target
4. Numbar
5. Mobot
6. Tivi
7. Lunino
9. Its heart beats
10. Makes up a song
11. Oibel
12. A butterfly
13. Lups
14. Moky
15. Lucky Rub

PAGES 66-67: WHOSE HEAD IS IT ANYWAY?!

A - 2
B - 12
C - 10
D - 6
E - 9
F - 4
G - 15
H - 11
I - 3
J - 14
K - 8
L - 1
M - 5
N - 13
O - 7

PAGE 79: HORRO HURRY!

PAGE 84: GOGO CROSSWORD!

Hidden Gogo is Erhon.

PAGE 96: ODD ONE OUT!

Gogo 1 – 1
Gogo 2 – 3
Gogo 3 – 2
Gogo 4 – 4

PAGES 102-103: KNOW YOUR SUPERSTARS!

1. Sato
2. Imooki
3. Helly
4. Sunon
5. Tsu
6. Tori
7. Misha
8. Divel

109

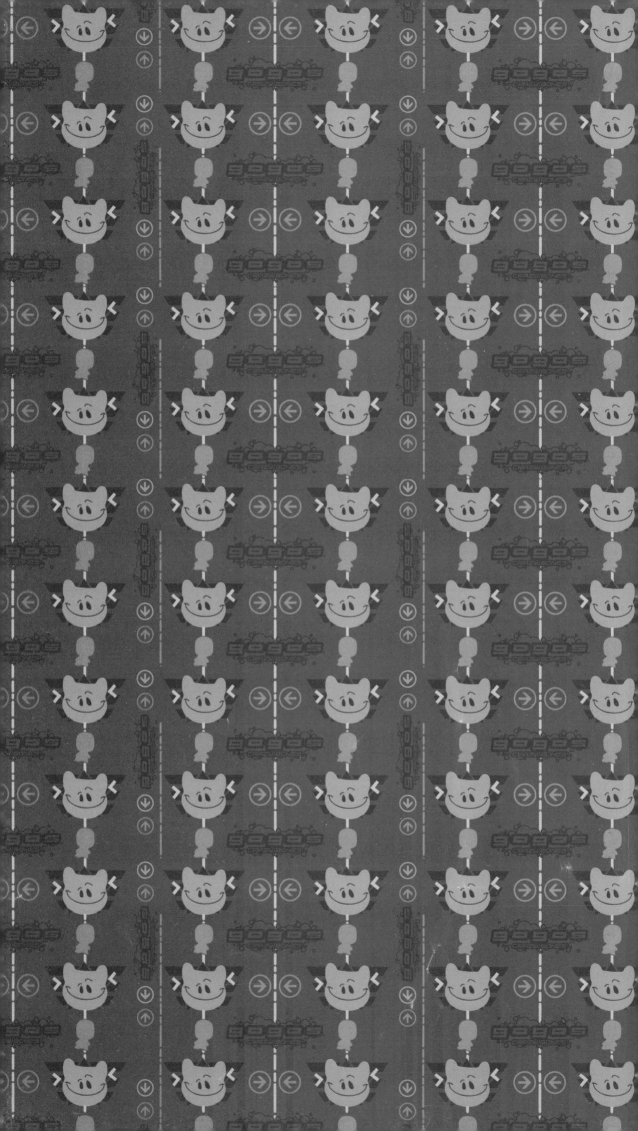